HEALERS
AND
HEALING

HEALERS
AND
HEALING

*Amazing cases from the
world's best-known healers*

ROY STEMMAN

PIATKUS

First published in 1999 by
Judy Piatkus (Publishers) Ltd
5 Windmill Street, London W1P 1HF

**The moral right of the author
has been asserted**

*A catalogue record for this book is available
from the British Library*

ISBN 0-7499-1887-X

Edited by Kelly Davis

Data capture & manipulation by
Phoenix Photosetting, Chatham, Kent
Printed and bound in Great Britain by
Butler & Tanner Ltd, Frome, Somerset

CONTENTS

CONTENTS

ACKNOWLEDGEMENTS

There are many people to whom I am indebted for both inspiration and practical assistance in the writing of this book. Many of them – such as healers I have known personally, including Harry Edwards, Ted Fricker, George Chapman and Doris Collins – are referred to in the following pages. Their dedication to helping others and the results they achieve have always impressed me greatly. The seeds they planted in my mind, when I discussed their techniques and beliefs, have grown into *Healers and Healing*.

My thanks to Judy Piatkus, who encouraged me to write this book, and editor Kelly Davis for their advice and assistance.

Above all, I would like to express my thanks to Danny Lee whose research contribution has played a major role in the preparation of this book. To these, and to everyone else who has helped me produce *Healers and Healing*, I offer my heartfelt thanks.

INTRODUCTION

During the 1960s I saw a number of British spiritual healers at work. Perhaps the most impressive, in terms of speed of results, was Ted Fricker, a larger-than-life Cockney healer who, at the height of his fame, had long queues of sufferers waiting outside his north London home each morning. He treated almost every disease but was particularly noted for his success with slipped discs and ulcers. His power to heal came from God, Fricker explained, but he knew precisely what to do and was able to diagnose his patients' conditions because of a voice that had spoken to him and guided him most of his life.

I spent a morning watching him at work in his small healing room from which there were two doors: one to the waiting room and one to his front door. He would sit the patient on an upholstered stool, find out the problem, turn up the music on his record player (whether classical or popular made no difference), then place his hands on the person and, after a short while, physically shake as if an electric shock were passing through his hands. In most cases, after this brief treatment, he told the patients they were better, and got them to prove it to themselves where possible.

I remember one woman, accompanied by her teenage son, who was crying in pain from a back problem aggravated by queuing for so long. Fricker's receptionist always ensured that people were seen by the healer strictly in the order in which they arrived, but the others took pity on the woman and allowed her to be seen first. She winced with pain as he helped lower her onto the stool. Then he turned the music up even louder than normal, placed his hands on both sides of her body and closed his eyes. When he told her she no longer had the problem she looked at him in disbelief, though she admitted the pain had gone. At Fricker's command she stood up unaided. I felt I could read her mind as she glanced first at her son and then at me. She had suffered so much pain, it was almost too good to believe.

'Sit down,' the healer said to her, nodding to a low arm-chair in the corner of the room.

'I can't,' she responded. 'I haven't been able to sit in a chair like that for ages.'

'Yes, you can,' Fricker insisted.

Slowly, she walked to the armchair and turned as if to sit down, but then she froze. It was clear that her biggest fear now was that the action of sitting would undo the healing and her body would once more be racked with pain.

'You can do it,' he said.

She began to bend her legs but stopped. Shaking her head, she maintained, 'I can't.'

Fricker was a busy man. There were other patients waiting for treatment and, as far as he was concerned, this patient was cured. Without further ado he reached out to her shoulders and gave her a gentle push. She lost her balance and fell back into the chair with a look of horror. Her son tried to grab her but was not quick enough. Instead of a shriek of pain, however, we all saw a huge grin spread across her face. She *was* cured. She stood up, unaided, and sat down again to prove it, before thanking Fricker profusely. He nodded an acknowledgement, said a few kind words and ushered them to the door. As he closed it behind them with one hand he was already opening the waiting room door with the other and calling in the next patient.

I decided to ask the woman a few questions and followed her and her son into the street outside. There were tears in her eyes once more, but this time they were of joy. And she was working her way down the queue, telling people what had just happened to her.

Later, in the middle of the morning, Fricker paused for a short break between patients. 'Would you like a drink?' he asked me, lifting the upholstered lid of the healing stool. Inside, to my great amusement, I found that his patients had been sitting on bottles of spirits. I think he poured himself a small whisky and, thus fortified, turned his attention once more to the stream of sufferers needing his help.

Becoming a patient

It may be fascinating to watch other people being healed but it is a poor substitute for receiving healing yourself. My own opportunity to receive healing came unexpectedly when I stretched across to switch off my alarm clock one morning. There was an audible click, followed by the rapid realisation that my head would not straighten. Worse, when I tried to look to the left, I was stopped by an excruciating pain. I didn't need a doctor to tell me that a disc had almost certainly popped out from between the vertebrae in my neck. I might have to wear a neck brace for weeks and perhaps even have traction before I was back to normal.

Instead of consulting my doctor, however, I called Leonard Morris, a healer. He did not give public demonstrations but had earned a reputation as a powerful healer simply by word of mouth. He agreed to see me later that day in his St John's Wood home in north-west London. Getting there was difficult. Since my head would not turn, I had to twist my entire body every time I crossed a road to ensure I was not run over.

Leonard Morris welcomed me and sat me on a dining chair in front of the fireplace in his elegant apartment. We had already discussed my problem on the telephone so he lost no time in starting the healing. Placing one hand on the back of my neck and the other on my forehead, he stood quite still for a few moments and then we began chatting. I was expecting to feel an intense sensation in the area of my neck where something had clearly got out of alignment. When I felt nothing – no warmth, cold, tingling or vibration – I concluded that, for whatever reason, I was not receptive to the healing power and that I would have to resort to more protracted, conventional medical treatment. Hanging on the wall was one of Leonard Morris's own paintings and I asked him what had inspired it. We talked for a couple of minutes, with his hands still firmly where he had placed them at the start of the session.

'OK,' he said, walking round in front of me. 'That's done. It's gone. But you're going to feel pain for a day or two more, because the area is inflamed. Just put a hot salt poultice on it to ease the pain and it'll be gone in a couple of days.'

My doubts must have registered on my face. Without saying anything he placed his fingers on my cheeks and moved my head from side to side. To my utter astonishment, my head now moved freely. There was no obstruction. I had felt and heard nothing, yet Leonard Morris *knew* that healing had taken place. And though the whole area still throbbed with pain, it was no longer a searing, dagger-like agony. All the way back home I kept moving my head from side to side, just to make sure it still worked. And sure enough, two days later, helped by the application of hot salt poultices just as he had recommended, all discomfort disappeared.

Now, whenever a sceptic tries to tell me healing is about manipulation or some other physical trickery, I can refute the argument from personal experience. And, though I was already convinced that healing was possible, in this particular case I was also certain that it was not taking place – so I am equally sure that my own 'faith' played no part in the result. I should add that I have never since been troubled by a return of that neck condition.

That was thirty-five years ago and I have received healing on only one other occasion since then. In 1997 I was visiting my old friends Doris Collins, Britain's top medium and healer, and her husband Philip, in their home near Milton Keynes in Buckinghamshire. It was, as always, a very enjoyable day, during which we talked about psychics and healers we knew and of our various experiences. However I had woken that morning with earache and had taken a couple of painkillers in the hope of shifting it; unfortunately it became increasingly uncomfortable. I believe there's a time and a place for everything, and the last thing I wanted to do was turn a social occasion into 'work' for Doris. Like anyone else, she needs to be able to separate her personal life from her other activities; otherwise there would be a never-ending stream of people seeking her help. But in the end I told myself that I should suffer no more, and I confided to her that my left ear was causing me considerable pain. Would she mind giving me healing?

'Of course I will,' she said, and Philip immediately found me a chair, with another facing it for his wife. She placed the fingers of one hand over the ear, and her other hand rested on my right hand, on my knee. As we sat there, she began getting psychic impressions and I received a spirit message as a bonus. The healing session was over in a few minutes and we returned to their beautiful sun lounge to relax and share further memories. I noticed only marginal improvement at the time of the healing, but by the time I reached my home in London that night the ear pain had totally disappeared. To some, this may seem a trivial example, but I mention it to show that the healing force can work at any time, in any place, so long as the healer is attuned to the source of that power.

Why write a book about healing?

These personal experiences made me want to investigate healing further. And, fortunately, my professional background had helped equip me to write a book on the subject.

For more than ten years I wrote for the weekly Spiritualist newspaper *Psychic News* and was its assistant editor for a large part of that time. Since healing plays a very prominent role in the Spiritualist movement, I was in a unique position to get to know most of the UK's top healers and see them at work. Satisfied by these experiences that healing could often be very effective, I never hesitated to recommend that friends or relatives consult healers when they were not responding to conventional medical treatment. And, naturally, I was ready to practise what I preached.

I remember when one of my uncles was rushed into hospital and given just hours to live. I phoned my good friend George Chapman, a trance healer then living in Aylesbury, and asked if the spirit doctor who works through him could arrange for distant healing to be sent to my uncle. Not only did he survive, but the doctors decided next day that he did not need the life-saving operation they had thought would be necessary. I subsequently collaborated with Chapman on a couple of books, including *Surgeon from Another World*, collecting testimonies from showbusiness personalities, royalty and doctors.

For nearly a decade, hardly a week went by without me writing either a feature or a news story about healing. I watched Harry Edwards, the most famous healer of recent times, attract thousands of people to venues such as the Royal Albert Hall and the Royal Festival Hall in London and I spoke to the people he healed. There was no denying that he produced remarkable results in most cases. He welcomed doctors and sceptics onto the platform to check the patients before and after the treatment. He, and later Tom Johanson, another British healer, even gave healing demonstrations in Trafalgar Square.

A few years after leaving *Psychic News* a journalist friend, David Harvey, and I decided to launch our own magazine on the paranormal, called *Alpha*, and once again healing was one of the subjects we covered. In fact David is the author of an excellent book on the subject (*The Power to Heal*) and in an early issue we featured one of the remarkable healers he met during his research – John Cain of Liverpool. Not only did Cain have an impressive ability to cure people of their illnesses but he did so in a surprising way. Many of those who consulted him would fall into a faint or a trance as soon as he put his hands on them . . . and when they recovered they were cured of their ailments.

Seeing, as they say, is believing. And what I witnessed was beyond doubt. But for much of that time I was merely reporting events, for I did not feel willing or able to even begin to explain what was happening in such cases. Even some of the healers I spoke to had no real idea about where their healing powers came from or how they worked. They believed they just provided a channel to be used for the good of others. Indeed, they said it could be argued that knowing too much about the 'mechanics' might inhibit what they did. For me, it has always been important to know the answers to such questions. But it is only in recent years, as my knowledge of other paranormal phenomena has expanded, that I have begun to formulate a theory.

For the past five years I have been producing *Reincarnation International Magazine*, a quarterly publication which looks at the large body of evidence which suggests we may all have lived before, and can look forward to many more lives in the future. Here again, healing plays a very significant role, for there are many therapists who use past-life regression to treat their patients. They believe that some of us bring into this life problems from our previous earthly existence and we can shed these problems – which are frequently fears and phobias – by bringing them to the surface, usually under hypnosis, and then letting go of them. Is this fantasy or fact? Whichever it is, it seems to work incredibly effectively for many individuals.

I am not a scientist. Nor do I claim that my thoughts are special or unique – indeed, I frequently quote many others who are thinking along similar lines. But I do have the advantage of being able to draw on a very broad experience of healing, stretching back over thirty years.

Healing, as I see it, is part of a far bigger picture. There is a new realisation about the nature of man and the interconnectedness of all of us, not only with each other but with everything else in the universe. It's a difficult concept to grasp perhaps, but only something so all-embracing can begin to explain the astonishing range of spiritual, mental and physical events which are grouped together under the name of 'healing'.

Why investigate healing?

For many people ill-health is not a condition they have to accept – despite what they may have been told by doctors. There are countless authenticated cases of individuals who have made an astonishing return to perfect health contrary to established medical opinion.

The human body has remarkable self-healing abilities and, left to its own devices, can often be relied upon to engineer, in time, a measure of improvement in many conditions. The case studies I will be examining in this book, however, suggest that there are also external healing forces, independent of the body's own recuperative powers, which can hasten our return to health.

This is not a book about alternative medicine. The individuals cited may well have tried acupuncture, aromatherapy, homeopathy, herbalism or any one of a bewildering range of other 'physical' therapies, but it is an invisible, 'spiritual' healing power that we are in search of.

Although there are many methods which appear to harness such a power, I will not be attempting to measure their effectiveness in treating specific conditions, for the very simple reason that what works for you may not work for me. Though *all* the healing techniques discussed in these pages have been shown to work for certain individuals, some people inevitably respond better to one type of treatment than another.

A quick glance at this study may lead you to conclude that there are many different healing forces at work. However, my own view is that there is a single healing power, freely available to everyone, which has been labelled differently around the world according to local cultural or religious beliefs. The methods I will examine are just various attempts – all of them successful – to harness it to best effect. Ultimately, we should judge spiritual healing by its results, not by the sometimes bizarre techniques employed, or even by the occasionally suspect motives of those who call themselves healers – just as we should judge a good wine by its taste, not by the vessel in which it is served.

Healing remains a mystery. But so, too, does electricity. You don't have to understand how the latter works in order to take advantage of lighting, heating or television. If you, or someone you know, suffers from poor health, don't let your lack of understanding of how healing works prevent you from trying it – if conventional medical treatment is not producing results. All you have to do to benefit from the healing light, metaphorically speaking, is to press the switch.

I hope that this book will make you more comfortable about doing so and that the results will live up to your expectations. After all, as you are about to find out, the case studies I quote – a mere fraction of those available – demonstrate clearly that, with healing, *anything* is possible.

1

THE HEALING TOUCH

For millennia people have believed that certain individuals could heal the sick simply by touching them. The global explosion of interest in the healing arts that we are witnessing today is not, therefore, a new phenomenon. But is there any scientific basis for this sort of healing? And who are the people who claim to have these powers?

In ancient civilisations they were the healer-priests. In other cultures they are known as shamans, witchdoctors or folk healers. Their roles in their respective societies may differ but the fact that their techniques are often remarkably similar suggests they are all harnessing the same healing force.

The historical perspective

The father of modern medicine, Hippocrates, was not only aware of such a power but used it himself. He wrote the following passage around the turn of the fifth century BC, but it describes the same phenomenon experienced by healers today:

> . . . that the heat which oozes out of the hand, on being applied to the sick, is highly salutary . . . It has often appeared, while I have been soothing my patients, as if

there was a singular property in my hands to pull and draw away from the affected place, and by extending my fingers towards it. Thus it is known to some of the learned that health may be implanted in the sick by certain gestures, and by contact, as some diseases may be communicated from one to another.

Hippocrates acknowledged that he was not unique in this. Other 'experienced doctors', he wrote, had noted the same sensation.

Earlier, probably around 1200 BC, another physician named Aesculepius produced remarkable healing results which, many testified, included bringing the dead back to life. He was immortalised as the Greek god of medicine, son of Apollo, and hundreds of temples were built to him. Here, the sick would sleep so that Aesculepius could appear to them in their dreams and heal them.

Of course, Jesus Christ was also said to have the ability to bring the dead back to life. His healing powers and techniques tend to be viewed differently, on the basis that he was the Son of God, and special. But he used the laying-on-of-hands, and other methods, to heal all manner of disease and told his disciples to do likewise. 'He that believes in me will also do the works I do, because I go to the Father. Whatever you ask in my name, I will do it.' (John, 14: 12–13). *The Bible* tells us that the apostles successfully followed Jesus's lead and it describes them curing blindness, dysentry and snake bite. These events have persuaded some people that only Christians can heal, through Jesus.

It was not only those acting under divine influence who could cure the sick. There is a long tradition of royal healers, which can be traced back to the third century BC. In those days, it was King Pyrrhus of Epirus who, astonishingly, was said to have the power to cure colic by the laying on of *toes*. But it was the hands of King Robert the Pious of France and King Edward the Confessor of England, in the eleventh century, which were used to treat the sick. The power to heal, it was decided, was hereditary to both the French and English thrones. For reasons we no longer understand, scrofula (which became known as 'the King's Evil') was soon singled out as the disease they could treat successfully. Scrofula was the early name used for tuberculosis of the bones and lymphatic glands and it sometimes resulted in dreadful disfigurement of its victims.

The 'King's Touch' was much in demand, with the tradition reaching its zenith in the seventeenth century when sufferers had their sores touched by the monarch and were then blessed. They also received a coin to hang around their necks. Charles II is said to have touched 90,798 sufferers in nineteen years, though whether this was because he believed in his own powers, or was simply pleased that others did, we do not know. The cost to the country of the King's Touch was high, however, since each sufferer generally received a gold coin.

And the gift of healing scrofula was not confined to the monarchy, though those who believed they had special powers were not always eager to publicise the fact. Valentine Greatrakes was an exception . . . eventually. A former cavalry lieutenant in Ireland who fought for Cromwell, Greatrakes became a Justice of the Peace and owned a large estate in County Waterford, Ireland, becoming its High Sheriff in 1666. By then he already had a reputation with the sick, following 'an impulse or strange persuasion' to heal. He became convinced that he had 'the gift of curing the King's Evil, which for the extraordinariness thereof, I thought fit to conceal for some time', encouraged by his wife dismissing the idea as 'idle imagination'.

However, Mrs Greatrakes had to change her mind when her husband, while accompanying her on a charitable mission to dispense medicine to the poor, decided to test his power. He laid his hands on the eyes, throat and cheeks of a boy suffering 'grieviously' from scrofula 'and prayed to God for Jesus's sake to heal him'. A few days later, the father brought the son, in Greatrakes' own words, 'with the eye so much changed that it was almost quite whole, and to be brief (to God's glory I speak it) within a month he was perfectly healed and so continues.'

George Fox, founder of the Society of Friends (known as the Quakers) was healing the sick during the same period and kept careful records of his cures, achieved in England and America. But he did not publish his 'Book of Miracles' for fear of attracting ridicule to the new movement.

Although many of these healers were working in the name of God or Jesus, there was a growing suspicion in some communities that demons, or the Devil himself, had a hand in the cures. In other words, they believed these cures were the result of witchcraft or black magic – and the Devil had cured the sufferer in return for his soul. On the other hand, confusingly, there were healers who maintained that illnesses were *caused* by demonic possession and they produced their cures by conducting exorcisms on the sick.

This lack of a unified theory probably helps to account for the changing degrees of acceptance of healing over the centuries, at least outside orthodox religion. What is beyond doubt is that it is now enjoying unparalleled acceptance around the globe and even within the medical profession – some doctors even practise healing – despite the fact that we are still a long way from understanding how or why it works.

Harry Edwards' healing crusade

Healing owes much of its current popularity in the West to Spiritualist healers who laid an impressive foundation in the mid-1900s, on which many others are now building reputations and, in a few cases, fortunes. The doyen of post-war British healers was Harry Edwards, a cherubic former printer who gave up his job to devote his life to healing the sick and writing about his experiences. Edwards' healing crusade was undoubtedly the most significant of recent times. His public demonstrations drew thousands and he always invited any medical professionals in the audience to join him on the platform to examine the person seeking help before healing began.

There was nothing theatrical about Edwards, though he did make a point of choosing demonstrable problems at his public performances. He was a good communicator who made sure his audience knew the nature of each sufferer's condition and the limitations it imposed, as well as the medical prognosis, before he and his assistants started healing. The treatment consisted simply of laying on hands and a short period of silence. There was no manipulation. Yet many of the sufferers were instantly transformed. Some were able to throw away their crutches and walk off the stage. Others bent and touched their toes for the first time in years. Others said their sight or hearing had dramatically improved. Usually Edwards would advise them to have two or three more healing sessions to effect a lasting result, and those who could easily get to his sanctuary at Burrows Lea in Shere, Surrey, were invited to do so. Edwards' work is carried on there today by Ray and Joan Branch who assisted him in his work before his death in 1976.

After watching many of Edwards' public healing demonstrations, I joined a group of sufferers at Burrows Lea in the 1960s to see how he dealt with them privately. His beautiful sanctuary was tranquil and soothing and those who had appointments with him sat quietly in a large circle. They did not receive one-to-one consultations but, in effect, experienced a scaled-down version of his larger demonstrations, which meant they all witnessed each other's experiences.

One woman's severe back pain made it very difficult for her to bend. Edwards turned to me and asked me to pull my chair closer to his and place my hand on the small of her back, where the pain was most severe. He then put his right hand over mine and his left on her abdomen. We sat like that for no more than a minute.

'What do you feel?' he asked her.

'Heat,' she responded. 'It feels very warm.'

Edwards smiled and looked at me. 'And you?'

'Nothing,' I told him.

His smile broadened and he nodded. Later, he explained why. My hand did not need healing so the power passed straight through it and into the woman whose suffering he was seeking to alleviate. I felt nothing because I needed no help. She felt heat because the healing power was working on her condition. Sure enough, she reported that the pain had lessened and she was able to bend with ease.

Harry Edwards' explanation was deceptively simple, for it suggested that healing was just about the transfer of energy. In fact, he believed that the act of healing was a very complex affair and that he and the thousands of others who worked in a similar way were mediums for highly skilled physicians and their helpers *in the spirit world*. They used him as a channel for the power they generated, carefully controlling and directing it to deal with each specific problem they encountered. All he had to do was to attune himself to them: *they* did the healing.

Edwards was aware that some observers might conclude that sufferers made *themselves* better through the strength of their belief in his powers but he refuted that. How could the body respond with such speed, curing slipped discs, reducing goitres and other growths, bringing movement back into limbs that had not moved in some cases for many years? The sceptics, he insisted, had no answer. All the evidence pointed to an *intelligence* behind each healing, which knew exactly what was needed to restore a sick body to normality or to start the healing process. That intelligence came from his team of spirit doctors who, he believed, included Louis Pasteur. (The case for discarnate involvement in healing will be dealt with in greater detail in Chapter Six.)

Healing can happen anywhere

Doris Collins and her husband Philip were once preparing to fly from London's Heathrow Airport for a holiday in the sun. They had boarded the aircraft and were waiting for the pre-flight safety announcement when she suddenly recognised a good friend making his way down the centre aisle, accompanied by a stewardess. It was Donald Saunders, an American hotelier, who had known Doris Collins for many years. They had spoken on the telephone a few days before and he had noted the coincidence that they would both be at Heathrow at about the same time on the same day: she to depart for a holiday and he in transit for Switzerland from the USA. But he had suddenly been afflicted by severe back pain and decided to take advantage of his close proximity to Doris. He managed to find out what flight she was on and persuaded ground staff to allow him to board her aircraft, accompanied by a stewardess, to ask for healing.

'There was nowhere to do the healing on the aircraft and I couldn't get off, so he had to sit on my knee,' she laughed. 'But I was able to put the back right and Donald completed his journey without further pain and we went off to enjoy our holiday.'

Doris Collins sometimes refers to herself as 'the bionic woman' because she has had so many surgical operations. 'I was made for the knife,' she joked, on returning home after making an astonishingly quick recovery from an artificial hip operation. It is a fallacy that healers never get ill. I know some who have never needed to consult a doctor in their entire lives, and others who know what suffering is all about from personal experience. Healers, after all, are only human and some are as susceptible as the next person to ill-health. In fact, serious illness is what introduces some individuals to their own healing powers in the first place.

'You can heal, too'

Ted Fricker, mentioned earlier, satisfied himself that he was a healer by treating his five-year-old daughter Theresa. She had been born with clusters of warts on both hands and her parents had spent considerable sums of money unsuccessfully seeking a treatment. Within twenty-four hours of giving healing to his daughter the warts had disappeared without trace, and Ted soon decided to devote himself to healing.

One of the thousands who were grateful that he made that decision was Sussex businessman Maurice Tester who had suffered a prolapsed intervertebral disc between the fourth and fifth lumbar vertebrae while practising his golf swing. The injury failed to respond to other treatments but was eventually cured by Fricker after six or seven sessions. On his last visit, Ted Fricker astonished him by telling him, 'You are a healer, too. A born healer. You can do for others what I have done for you.' Events were to prove him right. Maurice Tester became a renowned healer, also specialising in slipped discs, simply by laying hands on the sufferers who sought his help. TV film director and ceramics expert Cyril Frankel was one of them. He, too, was cured and is now also an established healer, using the laying-on-of-hands to overcome the sickness of those who seek his help.

The power of touch

The power of touch is something that is instinctively understood. Many people, if they are not constrained by their upbringing or the pressures of society, express themselves freely by touching or hugging. This physical closeness has no sexual overtones: it occurs irrespective of gender and is simply a tactile way of showing concern, support or compassion. Parents are well aware of the power of touch – whether real or imaginary – with their children. A bump or a bruise can soon be 'rubbed' better by a caring parent. Research at McGill University in Montreal has also indicated that high levels of physical contact in the early days after birth can drastically reduce the chances of children developing stress-related diseases in later life.

The healing power of touch has also been highlighted by the work of Dolores Krieger, a nurse who pioneered its use in hospitals in the 1970s. Since then it has become known as 'therapeutic touch', though this is slightly misleading since it does not involve physical contact. Instead, in a calm but concentrated frame of mind, the person using this technique allows his or her hands to travel 4 to 6 inches (10–15 cm) above the patient's body, trying to sense areas of excess energy. The purpose of therapeutic touch is to redistribute that energy and so relieve tensions and symptoms of illness, thus promoting good health.

It may sound like mumbo jumbo but between 20,000 and

30,000 nursing staff are now said to incorporate it into their routine care of children and adults. For them, it might seem like a new idea but 15,000-year-old cave paintings in the Pyrenees depict similar images of caring touch. Perhaps these are the earliest recorded healers?

But that still leaves us with the question: how can touch have such an impact on health? In the UK, the Royal College of Nursing conference in York in May 1998 heard of two, as yet unpublished, research projects involving different forms of massage. Though these were not directly concerned with healing, they show that touch does have a powerful impact on our health.

Carol Cox, an intensive-care nurse at St Bartholomew's Hospital in London, told the conference of tests that had been carried out on forty-three patients in a major trauma centre using reflexology (a form of touch therapy which involves massaging and pressing on very specific points on the feet to produce certain responses in the body). According to Mrs Cox the use of reflexology did produce physiological changes, though the changes weren't always desirable. When pressure was applied to the arch of the foot, the medical researchers found that there was a significant drop in the heart rate, blood pressure and respiratory rate. As 'intensive-care nursing is particularly concerned with maintaining blood pressure,' she explained, 'this kind of foot massage has to be questioned as it relates to treatment in a special unit.' After this word of warning, however, Mrs Cox went on to say that tests on fifty-three other neurological patients indicated there were benefits and no risks from other less focused techniques, such as general massage and manipulation, which were particularly helpful in promoting rest and relaxation.

She also told of research carried out on premature babies in Wolverhampton using a touch technique called 'tic-tac' which seemed to help them overcome the trauma of being born early. Those babies who received the treatment appeared to be 'more relaxed and there was less movement'. Why should this be?

What reflexologists and the practitioners of some other

forms of massage have in common with therapeutic touch healers is the belief that the body has an energy system which, when out of balance, causes sickness. Touch, massage, even just the presence of the hands of a balanced person – the healer – is apparently sufficient to rid the patient of blockages and get the energy flowing again.

One of the fastest-growing forms of spiritual healing, Reiki, is based on this principle. It originated in Japan and its founder was Dr Usui, a Tokyo Spiritualist and psychic, who is said to have discovered the secret of Reiki on a sacred Japanese mountain. He started a healing society in 1922 and began treating people and lecturing. Much of our knowledge of Dr Usui comes from one of his students, Mrs Takata, who not only seems to have been responsible for the introduction of Reiki to the West but also for one of its more surprising developments – the decision to charge a $10,000 fee for a Reiki Mastership.

Reiki – pronounced 'ray-kee' – translates as 'spiritually guided life-force energy' and is said to be a technique for transmitting subtle energy to yourself or to others. Its practitioners perform a series of passes over the patient's body without touching it, and these are said to reduce stress, open blockages in the meridians, nadas and chakras – the rivers and streams of our energy bodies – and restore balance and vitality.

The idea of charging high fees for passing on such knowledge to others seems at odds with the spiritual aims of Reiki, and astonishes many other healers who regard their healing powers as a God-given gift. I have as yet seen no evidence that a person who becomes a Reiki Master displays special healing powers he or she did not have before parting with their money for the Reiki training, though I don't doubt that many are good healers. I also question why individuals would pay such large sums of money to become healers, unless they felt it was a good financial (or spiritual) investment.

The good news is that, apparently, a Reiki Master can choose to charge you much less – or nothing at all – if he or she so desires. The bad news is that there is talk of making trademarks of some of the names used in Reiki, which will deepen suspicions about commercialisation by some individuals involved in what, presumably, began as a noble form of healing with little concern for reward.

Putting aside such controversies, the growing importance of the healing arts is reflected in the ever-increasing numbers of people consulting healers, and the large amount of research being done on different forms of massage therapy and therapeutic touch.

Having established the importance of touch, we need to ask another question: how can some healers produce cures when touch is out of the question because the sufferers they treat successfully are far away?

And lastly, but perhaps most important of all: do we *all* have the power to heal?

These are issues I will be looking at in the chapters that follow.

2
HEALING AT A DISTANCE

If healing were just about touch, it might be possible to construct a simple theory of energy transfer that would satisfy believers and sceptics alike. But it is not. Any attempt to explain what healing power is and how it works must provide satisfactory explanations for a wide range of related phenomena, some of which – as we shall see – seem to challenge not only the laws of logic but also the laws of physics.

Take, for example, the well-documented claims made on behalf of 'absent' or 'distant' healers, who do not meet their patients. Indeed, in some cases, the sufferer is even unaware that healing power is being sent in his or her direction, yet still makes a recovery that surprises doctors, friends and relatives.

Before trying to understand how distant healing works, let me establish its reality by describing a few cases.

Totally cured in four days

An early example of distant healing concerns Prince Alexander Leopold Franz Emmerich von Hohenlohe-Waldenburg-Schillingfürst, who became a Catholic priest early in the nineteenth century. At the age of twenty-seven he discovered that he could cure the sick by praying for them, laying his hands on them or just commanding them to be

healed. Inevitably, there was pressure from the medical profession to cease this work but his aristocratic origins appear
to have given him more protection than most. By 1821 he
had devised a way of helping more people than he could by
contact healing. He announced that at certain hours of the
day he would be offering up a special mass for the sick at his
church in Bamberg, Bavaria, and invited those who were ill to
join him at the same time in prayers.

Among those who were successfully treated by this distant
healing was a young English novice nun who had suffered an
infection in her thumb which spread to her arm and shoulder.
Her wrist had swelled to 15 inches (38 cm) in circumference
and, after eighteen months of unsuccessful medical treatment, amputation seemed to be the only solution. The day
after that advice was given, von Hohenlohe included her
name in one of his special masses and at the very same time it
was noted that the swollen wrist began to diminish in size. By
the same evening, the wrist's circumference was only 5 inches
(13 cm) and within four days she was totally cured.

Death-bed miracle

An even more dramatic result was brought about by the same
Catholic healer on 10 March 1824. A plea for distant healing
was sent to von Hohenlohe from the United States where the
sister of the Mayor of Washington was lying paralysed and
dying. A group of people gathered at her bedside at 3.30 am
in order to coincide with the time of the special Bavarian
mass at which her name was to be mentioned. What happened next was reported in the *Catholic Spectator*:

> At the moment of receiving the Blessed Sacrament
> (which, her tongue being quite parched and dead-like,
> she could hardly effect) she rises up in her bed, and
> lifting up her two arms, one of which she had not been
> able for a long time even to move, she exclaims – 'Lord
> Jesus, what have I done to obtain so great a favour?
> What shall I do to acknowledge so great a benefit?',

asks for her clothes, dresses herself, sits up, throws herself down on her knees with the priest, the Rev. Stephen Dubuisson, who had given her holy communion, and who was prostrate on the ground, lost in a transport of admiration and gratitude, then rises, walks through the room, and on that same morning took as much food as she had taken for the space of six months previous . . .

On that very same day she is said to have received a thousand visitors and that number doubled next day. She further astonished her physicians by shaking hands with each one of them!

Taken home to die

Harry Edwards tells of a boy in Sheffield, England, who contracted a disease at the age of three which baffled medical experts. He lost his appetite, his body became emaciated and he began swaying from side to side. Various specialists examined him over a seven-year period and he spent several periods in hospital, but none of the treatments seemed to benefit him at all. Eventually he was taken to London's top children's hospital where he was examined by one of the country's leading physicians. By then, the swaying had become more pronounced and he was suffering from paralysis of the legs. The experts' verdict was that there was nothing that could be done for the boy, and so his relatives took him home to die.

However, his elder sister had read about Edwards and decided to write to him, as 'a last hope', asking for distant healing for her brother. 'Within three weeks the swaying stopped and the boy began to take his food,' Edwards writes in *The Power of Healing*. 'The body built up and gathered strength, the signs of paralysis disappeared and, before very long, he became normal in every way.' He was able to go to school, where he took part in sport and recreation, and he also passed his academic examinations with flying colours. From the moment distant healing began he had no medical treatment of any kind and, having moved with his family to Yarmouth, they had not bothered to register him with a doctor.

This remarkable case was submitted to the Archbishops' Commission whose special committee of doctors, appointed by the British Medical Association, considered it along with others. They decided, however, that 'as the boy no longer had a doctor to whom the committee could refer, no investigation could take place'.

Three hours from death

Another case referred to Edwards was that of a young woman who became so ill with bulba polio that she was flown to London from Kenya in 1957, then transferred to a Brighton hospital. As soon as she arrived she was given a tracheotomy because her paralysed throat muscles made it impossible for her to swallow liquids or take food. She had also lost the power of speech. Her account of that dreadful illness, in a letter to Edwards, written after her full recovery, contains this passage:

> In hospital I was being fed through a nose tube. My ability to breathe was extremely poor and the following day, August 18th, I was put onto an automatic breathing machine. At 9am on the morning of August 20th when my brother came to see me he was told that I was not expected to live more than another three hours. My aunt, Lady Baden-Powell, on hearing this news, contacted you at once at the Sanctuary, Shere, asking for your help. The paralysis by that time had affected my neck and my brain and the top half of my body was threatening to close in on my heart. My heartbeats were getting slower and slower. My left lung had stopped operating altogether and report has it that my eyes were completely sunken in a death-like mask. At 5pm I was still alive. My mother arrived from Kenya and I was just able to recognise her. To the doctors and

nurses attending me it was a miracle that I survived that day and the following night. I personally did not know until long after I was off the danger list – in fact until several months later – that you had been contacted and that you and your healers had been, and were giving me, spiritual help through absent healing.

By the time this testimony was published in Edwards' book, the young woman concerned was back on her Kenyan farm, helping her husband with all aspects of its management, riding extensively and showing no signs of ever having had polio.

The healing minute

During the Second World War, Harry Edwards established the Healing Minute. At 9pm Greenwich Mean Time, Edwards and his helpers would send out their healing thoughts around the world and those who wished to receive them had only to pause at the same time and open their hearts and minds to the power that was being transmitted.

Edwards also tried his own distant healing experiment when the Asian flu epidemic was sweeping the world and heading for Britain. Through the pages of *The Spiritual Healer* magazine, and in some 20,000 letters to his regular patients, he and his team announced that they would be holding a mass absent healing intercession for all the readers of the publication and all their patients, to give them and their families protection against the dreaded influenza. In order to check the efficacy of the experiment they asked to be informed of all cases of flu suffered by those they were hoping to protect.

The epidemic eventually struck, affecting a large proportion of the population, particularly in the Midlands and the North of England. Factories and schools closed and many people died. Yet Edwards' sanctuary was informed of only twenty or so cases of people being hit by the bug, even though, according to national statistics, between 500 and

1000 infections would have been expected. Nor were any of the healers or helpers at the Burrows Lea Sanctuary affected by Asian flu.

At the height of his healing career, Edwards was receiving hundreds of letters a day from people all over the world pleading for his help. He could give personal appointments to only a very few individuals, but he tried to help everyone through distant healing. It was, he has written, his main mission in life. In his book *The Evidence for Spirit Healing* he tells of over ten thousand incidents of 'super-normal healings' over a four-year period. Spiritualist healers like Edwards believe that what they do differs greatly from just praying for the suffering, though to an outsider it is at times difficult to distinguish between the two. All too often, Edwards explained, the words 'I will pray for him' are spoken without any real intent: almost like an expression of sympathy. Distant healing, he said, is 'prayer plus directive intercession through attunement with God's healing ministers in spirit, who administer the healing directive'.

According to Edwards, one of the most common experiences reported by those who are receiving distant healing is the awareness of a feeling of inner upliftment and new strength, as soon as the help commences. Edwards believed that the healing came from a large team of doctors and specialists in the spirit world whose mission was to respond to the needs of his patients, either by directing healing energies through his hands during personal consultations, or by visiting those patients unable to travel to Edwards' healing sanctuary and treating them spiritually. His invisible helpers, the spirit doctors, he added, had no trouble locating the person for whom healing had been requested, and the results were as beneficial for someone living on the other side of the world as for a next-door neighbour.

How does distant healing work?

All this still begs the question, 'How does it work?' Those who give advice on developing the power to heal tend to use pseudo-scientific terms which shed no real light on the mechanics. The National Federation of Spiritual Healers (NFSH), for example, explains that absent healing is done by spiritual healers, either individually or in a group, 'who attune with the Divine source to beam healing energies to the patient'. It adds that this treatment 'is at a level beyond the physical and evidence shows that it can be very effective, particularly in the treatment of young children, in cases of mental illness and in drug and alcohol addiction.'

Attuning to the Divine and beaming healing energies to patients may come easily to some, but such terminology sounds closer to science fiction than to spiritual science. And why should absent healing be so effective with the young, with the mentally disturbed and with addicts? The NFSH offers no explanation for this statement, nor evidence on which we can make our own judgement.

Then again, its explanation is no worse than most others that have been put forward over the years. The simplest is the theory that the healing force radiates out from the healer until it finds the patient. But how does it do that, and does anyone who 'gets in the way' also benefit from it? We also know that sound, light, magnetism and other forms of energy are affected by distance, yet healing is not. Patients who are thousands of miles from the healer report improvements or cures. Some form of telepathy or extra-sensory perception might be involved, since there are well-documented cases of people 'knowing', for example, that someone many miles away has died. But that won't convince most sceptics, since they are equally doubtful about the existence of ESP.

Then there is the spirit hypothesis, which suggests that there is a spiritual equivalent to the National Health Service in the spirit world, with teams of paramedics who float off to treat the sick whenever they receive an emergency call. This is probably the most difficult theory of all to swallow. But so many healers subscribe to it that we should not dismiss it without further consideration.

No need for appointments

When psychic healer Betty Balcombe wants to direct healing to patients at a distance, she uses photographs of the sufferers or, failing that, puts their names on pieces of paper. 'Sit quietly at the chosen time with your photographs and names face down in front of you,' she advises. 'Breathe deeply. Look at the first picture or name, then look in front of you and imagine an upright human shape.' She then describes the images and thoughts which the healer should focus on before repeating the same steps for each photograph or name. Balcombe recommends that this procedure be repeated at the same time each day – at least until an individual no longer needs absent healing – and says that departure from the set time is not a problem: the power will still be received. Even if the healer is unable to transmit the healing energy, or forgets to do so, 'the healing energy will automatically transmit for one or two days'.

This is good news for everyone involved. But there are those who argue that there may be no need even to put such a time limit on the healing. For example, Harry Edwards' home was wrecked in 1944 by a German bomb and his healing register was destroyed. He wrote later that the bottom fell out of his world 'for I knew that my absent healing work had received a very heavy blow. All I could then do was to recall from my memory as many cases as I could.'

At that time he was arranging for his patients to tune in at specific times for distant treatment. Naturally, he expected them to start reporting less progress in their conditions but was astonished when the opposite occurred. When he checked their responses he found that the percentage of improvements was actually improving. Edwards started to rethink the way in which he worked and realised that there was no need to make such appointments, except in emergencies. His new method was simply to make a mental note of the name of the person who wrote to him asking for healing help, leaving it to his spirit associates to do the rest.

Long after Edwards' death, his sanctuary continues to

transmit healing around the world, through the Healing Minute, and his co-workers Ray and Joan Branch continue to treat sufferers on a one-to-one basis. For them, and for others who specialise in absent healing, it is sufficient to know that it works.

On the road to recovery

Almost every healer soon becomes aware of the power of absent healing and puts it to good use, either when the numbers seeking help become too great to handle or a person is too sick, or too far away, to be treated in person.

That is what happened when Yorkshire healer Lorraine Ham was featured on the *Strange But True?* television series. Her phone began ringing the moment the credits started to roll and sackloads of correspondence were soon being delivered to her home. In a single day 600 letters arrived, and she eventually received – as a result of that appearance – a total of 20,000 requests for healing. Not surprisingly, she felt totally overwhelmed but was determined to help as many as possible. She enlisted the assistance of other healers around the country and formed a National Healing Centre which links them together. Three times a day, they meditate on those people Lorraine cannot see personally.

Among those who sought her help was athlete Ruth Dorrington who was struck down with a hip injury while preparing for the 1995 road racing season. Physiotherapy failed to overcome the problem and she had to curtail her training. When she saw Lorraine on TV she became convinced that this was the answer and wrote immediately. Dorrington was told that she would receive absent healing daily at 6.30am, 12.30pm and 10.30pm for six weeks and, though she confessed she really didn't understand what absent healing was, she said she began to feel better from that moment.

'The end of the six-week period coincided with the time when I felt I was fit enough to get back on to a proper training schedule and race seriously,' Dorrington told Jenny

Randles in *The Strange But True Casebook*. 'I wasn't sure if it was coincidence, or whether it was natural progression, but I felt the healing had definitely been a contributory factor.' She added that, after weeks of making little progress, the moment absent healing began, 'suddenly progress was all in the right direction'. And since receiving absent healing Dorrington has returned to top form and broken several club records.

Brain tumour disappears

Another who reports success with absent treatment is British healer Malcolm Southwood. His explanation of how it works is no more helpful than others: 'Everything that exists vibrates and has its own electromagnetic field which vibrates into space to be received by anything in harmony with it. It's just like receiving a radio signal.'

When a 43-year-old friend, Sue, reported she was troubled by severe headaches, Malcolm Southwood arranged to see her. They met in London where she revealed that she had a brain tumour which had failed to respond to radiotherapy treatment. Her consultant had told her she could expect to live no more than three months. After listening to her story, Southwood passed his hand over her head and she let out a scream. It felt, she explained, as if someone had put a red-hot needle through her brain. The healer told her to ring him whenever she had a pain and assured her that he would be sending her absent healing for her condition. She needed to call him on several occasions but, on following his directions to sit quietly and concentrate on him, the pain soon disappeared.

According to Malcolm:

> The three months came and went. She had by now
> stopped going to the hospital because there was nothing
> more they could do except offer her painkillers. After
> five months she needed no more treatment from me. By
> that time I had already told her that the tumour had
> gone and the hospital then confirmed it. During the

whole of that period we had not seen each other since the first meeting in London.

Putting it to the test

Much of the evidence for absent healing is anecdotal, but there have been attempts to submit it to scientific scrutiny. Robert Miller of the Holmes Center for Research in Holistic Healing in Los Angeles, California, for example, devised an elegant test over twenty years ago in which the subjects *did not know* they were taking part.

Dr Miller recruited a team of eight healers from different backgrounds and beliefs, including Olga Worrall, who was probably then America's best-known healer. They were asked to treat a series of patients suffering from high blood pressure by absent healing. Also participating in the project were several physicians, all unknown to the healers, who were asked to select and then monitor whether certain patients showed any alterations in diastolic blood pressure, systolic blood pressure, heart rate or general weight over a long period of time. But they did not know whether these patients were actually receiving absent healing or were simply part of the 'control' group. As for the healers, all they were told were the patients' initials, ages, general health condition and location. They were each expected to treat around six people in this way, and the experiment, which started in 1976, ran until 1979. During this time forty-eight people received healing and another forty-eight did not.

What this experiment showed was that four of the healers were particularly effective with absent treatment, producing 92 per cent improvement rates in their patients – compared with a 75 per cent improvement rate in control subjects receiving only conventional treatment. In his summing up of this project, D. Scott Rogo, author of *Mind Over Matter*, remarks:

> This is not a statistically significant result, but does show a trend in the data. Robert Miller's own

conclusions on the basis of his study are mixed. While
he is satisfied that the experiment has indeed
documented the existence of remote or 'absent' healing,
he has remained puzzled over the unsystematic nature
of his results.

Why, for example, did some patients show a greater improvement in their systolic blood pressure than their diastolic
blood pressure? Such questions continue to remind us that we
are still a long way from really understanding how healing
works, particularly distant healing.

Diagnoses at a distance

Asking sceptics to accept that a healer's mind can somehow
locate a stranger, maybe hundreds or even thousands of miles
away, simply on the basis of his or her initials, and pass on
healing energy at a distance, is surely expecting the impossible. But there are theories and experimental work which may
shed some light on what is happening.

Let us look first at the possibility of one human mind 'collecting' information from another person at a distance. One
of the earliest people to demonstrate this ability was the
American psychic Edgar Cayce who made diagnoses at a distance. He would go into a trance and his higher consciousness
would 'locate' a person whose name and address he was given.
Often he could describe the individual and what they were
doing at that precise moment. He also gave remarkably accurate reports on the state of health of many of these people,
including children, and went on to prescribe the treatment
they needed to help them overcome their health problems.

Every word Cayce spoke was recorded in shorthand and
the transcripts now form part of the massive archives of the
Association for Research and Enlightenment at Virginia
Beach, USA, which is dedicated to promoting Cayce's work.
The evidence suggests that, in his heightened state of awareness, Cayce's mind was able to travel vast distances and 'find'
the person and information requested.

Time and space no barrier

But the case for mind communicating with mind does not rest on just one American psychic. In 1997 scientists at Edinburgh University, Scotland, announced that they had new, striking evidence that extra-sensory perception – ESP – was fact, not fiction. A team led by Professor Robert Morris had been working with subjects in what is known as the Ganzfeld state. In a windowless, soundproof, and electromagnetically screened room, their normal vision and hearing is blocked and replaced with 'white noise' and they are then asked to describe any images that come into their mind. At the same time, a 'sender' concentrates on a picture, randomly selected from four, in an attempt to transmit information about it to the subject. The Edinburgh team reported a 50 per cent 'hit rate' during trials with more than 100 people. Commenting on these results, *The Sunday Telegraph's* Robert Matthews said:

> The results are 335,000 times more 'significant' than the level of evidence governments demand of pharmaceutical companies before they will let a new drug on to the market. In short, by all the normal criteria of scientific evidence, Prof Morris and his team at the Koestler Institute have finally proved that ESP exists.

And there's more. Evidence for 'seeing at a distance' has also come from an unlikely source – America's Central Intelligence Agency. Between 1972 and 1995 the CIA spent thousands of dollars on experiments which tested the ability of certain individuals to see places and events occurring many miles away. Known as 'remote viewing', they included the request that psychic Ingo Swann 'visit' Jupiter two years before the arrival of the *Voyager 1* spacecraft and report what he saw. He described a planet with a ring around it. This was recorded as a mistake by the CIA and Swann himself concluded that he had been looking at Saturn. But when

Voyager 1 reached the huge planet astronomers were amazed to see that it did, after all, have a ring around it.

In other experiments, Swann and fellow subjects were given map co-ordinates and asked to describe what they saw at these places. Many of them proved to be top secret enemy sites. The CIA's director, Admiral Stansfield Turner, even admitted in the late 1970s that they had used remote viewing to successfully locate an aircraft which had been shot down in Zaire and which could not be found using spy satellites.

When Professor Jessica Utts of the University of California, Davis, USA, was asked by the CIA to make a statistical analysis of all this research in the early 1990s, she concluded that there was only a one-in-130 probability that these repeated experimental findings were the result of chance. 'Anomalous cognition is possible and has been demonstrated,' she said. 'This conclusion is not based on belief, but rather on commonly accepted scientific criteria.'

Seeing inside a body

If an individual can send his or her mind to a remote location and describe what is there, then surely it can also look inside another human being and detect disease? This is precisely what Caroline Myss, a former journalist, has been doing for years – with outstanding success. In *The Creation of Health*, the book she wrote with neurosurgeon Dr Norman Shealy, this ability was described as 'intuitive diagnosis'. This is how it worked. With a patient sitting in his office in Missouri, Dr Shealy would telephone Caroline Myss and give her just the individual's name and birthdate. She would then give her immediate impressions about the person's health. Beginning with psychological conflicts, Myss was gradually encouraged by Shealy to be more specific about physical abnormalities.

As the doctor–psychic partnership developed. Myss found she could 'enter' the patient's body and speak as if she were that person. With the doctor's encouragement, she learned to travel around the body, describing the condition of each organ system.

In their book they present fifty examples of comparative intuitive and medical diagnoses, some of which are almost identical, word for word. Shealy estimates Myss's accuracy at 93 per cent, which he says is a 'fantastic accomplishment', adding: 'I have not seen anyone more accurate than Caroline. Not even a physician!'

Where is she when she makes these instant intuitive diagnoses? In New Hampshire, 1200 miles away. She says that this separation is actually helpful because it enables her to receive information 'that a more personal connection would otherwise tend to block'.

Beginnings of a theory

Some individuals, it seems, have the gift of healing. This could mean that they possess some special energy in their bodies which they transmit to others, and this somehow restores balance to the sufferer. Or it could simply be that we are all surrounded by a healing force, but certain individuals are better channels or conduits of that energy and have developed techniques to focus it on those who are sick. We will be examining these possibilities, and others, later.

The first step is to accept that, though our bodies are restricted in time and space, our minds are not. A healer practising absent treatment only has to think of the person in need and a sympathetic, almost telepathic 'attachment' forms between the two of them. The healing power can then pass between them just as easily as if the patient were in the same room and receiving hands-on treatment.

For many people, there is only one person or force to whom they can turn when they are in need and that is God. Their pleas for help are not addressed to a healer – even one who says he is just a channel for God's healing energy – but to the Supreme Being who, in their view, is the only one who can grant them freedom from their pain and suffering.

But are their prayers answered?

3

THE POWER OF PRAYER

One of Britain's most popular television actors, 65-year-old Bryan Mosley, had not appeared on screen for nearly six months following two serious heart attacks. There was even speculation that, because he was making such a slow recovery, the writers to TV's longest-running soap opera, *Coronation Street*, were planning to kill off the character he'd played for thirty-five years – shopkeeper Alf Roberts, OBE, twice mayor of Weatherfield. When he was first taken ill, his screen wife Audrey explained his absence by saying she had left him at the town hall talking about the millennium, but there was a limit to how often that excuse could be used.

Real life, however, came to the rescue, with a storyline that even the most adventurous scriptwriter might have been reluctant to use. Father-of-six Mosley announced that he had experienced a miraculous cure after visiting Lourdes.

The Roman Catholic actor was persuaded by his wife Norma to make a pilgrimage to the shrine of Our Lady at Lourdes in the foothills of the French Pyrenees during a summer holiday in the South of France in 1997. They joined thousands of others, hoping that the trip would be worthwhile and that Mosley would feel better or, at the very least, 'come to terms with whatever the future might hold for us'.

Everyone who goes to Lourdes, or one of the many other healing shrines around the world, does so because they believe that particular place has special qualities. Perhaps it exerts a divine power which its walls somehow absorbed when the vision of the Virgin appeared. Or perhaps, because of its divine significance, prayers are more likely to be heard and answered in its unique environment. Or is the water at Lourdes somehow impregnated with healing power? For many people, Lourdes and other shrines seem to radiate a very strong energy, so maybe it is this – or the power of their own minds – which triggers a healing response in some of them.

For someone with heart problems, the journey to Lourdes was debilitating and Bryan Mosley felt desperately ill as he crossed the French countryside to and from the shrine. But the effort was not in vain.

'Something special happened to me there,' he told the *Daily Telegraph's* Tom Utley in August 1997, soon after his return. 'It is nothing short of a miracle. I feel blessed.'

He told the journalist that, once he had returned from France and had a good night's rest, 'I woke next morning feeling really well, better than I've been for years. My faith is stronger and my health has rapidly improved – so much so that, God willing, I hope to be back in *Coronation Street*.'

It was a hope that was soon realised as Alf Roberts – looking somewhat thinner than when his wife 'left him at the town hall' – walked back into the lives of *Coronation Street's* millions of fans.

Though Mosley, his family and countless soap opera followers may regard the dramatic improvement in his health as a miracle, the Roman Catholic Church has other ideas. With commendable restraint, it has been resisting claims of the miraculous ever since a fourteen-year-old asthmatic peasant girl, Bernadette Soubirous, said she had seen a vision of a white-clad woman in a grotto on the outskirts of the town in 1858. Between February and July that year, the Virgin is said to have appeared eighteen times to Bernadette, identifying herself as 'the Immaculate Conception' and revealing the presence of spring water at the back of a cave. It was decided by the villagers that the Virgin Mary was drawing attention to the water's healing powers and the sick soon started claiming cures.

Pilgrims have been immersing their bodies in the icy 'holy water' ever since, though today it is fed by pipe to specially constructed baths. The Roman Catholic Church did nothing to encourage belief in the miraculous powers of Lourdes water at first and the grotto was boarded up until Napoleon III ordered that it be reopened. Then the Church set up a special commission which, after a protracted investigation, declared in 1862 that 'the Immaculate Mary, Mother of God, did really appear to Bernadette Soubirous . . . Our conviction is based on the testimony of Bernadette but more especially on the events which have occurred and which have no explanation save an intervention of God'.

The lure of Lourdes

Millions of pilgrims have poured into Lourdes ever since, in search of healing. Some six thousand have testified to the improvement they have derived from their devotion and their claims have been duly recorded by the Lourdes Medical Directorate. Yet only sixty-five cures have been recognised as miracles by the Roman Catholic Church during nearly one and a half centuries – a rate of just one every two years.

Changing medical attitudes to illness have also had an impact on the figures. Whereas seven miracles were recognised in the 1940s and ten in the 1950s, only one was authenticated in each of the following two decades. This is not a success rate designed to attract vast numbers of desperate sufferers . . . and yet, around five million people a year continue to seek physical well-being or spiritual upliftment at Lourdes. That is more than the number who go to Rome, Jerusalem or even Mecca, and it has transformed the tiny hamlet of 140 years ago into a huge tourist centre whose impressive natural beauty is tarnished by stalls selling plastic souvenir statues and garish T-shirts.

Anyone claiming to be healed at Lourdes is carefully examined. Only those who satisfy this initial process are passed to a 25-member international committee of specialists who carry out an exhaustive examination. Conditions that might have a psychological origin are rejected. Diagnoses are checked to verify their accuracy. And the treatment being received at the time of the visit to Lourdes is assessed to see if the cure could be attributed to it without the need for divine intervention. Only those which appear to be genuine cases of spontaneous remission from a serious disease have any chance of going on to a higher medical tribunal in Paris and eventually clearing the final hurdle at which an ecclesiastic tribunal declares a case to be a miracle.

Bone cancers cured

Two of the three most recent cases concern cancer cures. Vittorio Micheli, a 22-year-old Italian Alpine Corps member, was admitted to Verona military hospital in April 1962. Doctors had detected a sarcoma, a type of cancer, which had eaten into the bone at the top of his left leg. For more than a year he was immobilised in a huge plaster cast as his condition gradually deteriorated. Then he announced that he wanted to be taken to Lourdes. The specialists responded by replacing his plaster cast with a stronger one, and they used its removal as an opportunity to examine him once more. His hip, they discovered, was now grossly deformed, his leg was lifeless and they could feel no bone through the fleshy tumour. Yet, as soon as Micheli and his plaster cast were immersed in the water of Lourdes he felt cured. He described a sensation of electricity passing through his body.

Back in hospital in Italy, the pain eased and his appetite returned. Within four weeks he was walking, even though the X-ray showed no change in his hip. Eight months later it was a very different story. Repeat X-rays showed what doctors described as 'a remarkable reconstruction of the bony tissue of the pelvis'. In time, fitted with a special shoe to compensate for the difference in length between his legs, Micheli was able to return to work, hike in the mountains and even play sports. His case is now one of the sixty-five miracle cures recognised by the Church authorities.

The most recent, officially authenticated miracle is that of Delizia Cirolli, an Italian girl with inoperable bone cancer who showed no sign of the disease when she returned to her Sicilian village after a pilgrimage to Lourdes. The Church announced its acceptance of her miracle cure in 1989, after a twelve-year investigation. But for many thousands of others who form the daily procession of sick and dying, the journey to Lourdes is a huge disappointment. They leave in wheelchairs, on stretchers and crutches, just as they arrived, taking with them not only their pain and suffering but the unanswerable question, 'Why was I not healed?'

A recent account of a trip to Lourdes was shared with readers of the *Daily Telegraph* by Sue Corrigan, a doctor's daughter, who took her severely disabled seven-year-old son Shane. They joined 760 others from Arundel and Brighton on a half-mile-long, specially reserved train which included three ambulance cars for the more seriously ill. A team of thirty-five nurses and ten doctors accompanied the pilgrims. To her surprise, Corrigan discovered that most of the sufferers were making return journeys to Lourdes – some had been close on twenty times. So why do they go back when their medical condition remains unchanged?

Because, Corrigan suggests, 'the sick and disabled are revered as the most precious of God's children, treated with a kindness and a generosity of spirit that makes them feel extraordinarily valued and worthwhile.' She reported no physical benefit for Shane, but ended her article with the words of Dr Kevin Kelly, a Surrey GP and leader of the group's medical team who was on his eighteenth pilgrimage: 'This place calls forth extraordinary love and affection.'

Lourdes, it seems, is endowed with a healing power which, at the very least, has a tremendous impact on a handful of people each decade and touches many hundreds more. But where does it come from? Is it in the water? Is it in the air? Is it carried in the prayers of the millions who make the pilgrimage annually? Or is it in the minds of the believers?

It certainly wasn't 'all in the mind' in the case of Louis Olivari, a French Communist, electrician and would-be local politician, who was paralysed down one side after falling from a ladder. He was opposed to everything Lourdes stood for and ignored his wife's many pleas that he should seek the Virgin's help. Eventually, in the summer of 1956, he agreed to pay a visit. He did so without expecting a result and nothing he saw, as he watched crippled bodies being immersed in the water, changed his cynical attitude. He stood, aloof from those around him, as his turn to be dipped in the water approached. A blind boy, making his fifth visit to Lourdes, sensed Olivari's state of mind and called to him, 'Pray'. This moved the Frenchman, who responded with the words, 'God, if you exist, cure this boy who deserves it more than I do.' At that moment he felt faint and had to be dragged from the water and placed on the ground. It was then that he discovered his paralysis had gone. He could walk.

Knock – the Irish Lourdes

Lourdes is just one of a number of religious sites around the globe which is believed to possess healing powers. Another of these is Knock in Ireland, which also owes its existence to a vision of the Virgin Mary and two other figures, seen by villagers more than a century ago. Though not as famous as Lourdes, it attracts around a million visitors a year. The tiny community of Knock has been visited by the Pope and Mother Teresa and even has its own modern international airport, as well as a team of doctors – established in 1936 – to check the medical evidence of healings reported by pilgrims.

One of those who claim to have been cured is Marion Carroll, an Irish woman who was in an advanced state of decline from multiple sclerosis when she made her third visit to Knock. Her kidneys had become seriously infected shortly before she made the 50 mile (80 km) ambulance journey from her home in Athlone on 3 September 1989. She was convinced she was about to die, but when a bishop passed in front of her stretcher and blessed her she had a beautiful feeling 'like a whispering breeze, telling me that if the stretcher was opened up then I could get up and walk'. Among those present was Dr John O'Meara and his wife Nuala who had known Marion Carroll since she was a child. They witnessed what happened after Marion asked for the straps on the stretcher to be untied. This is her own testimony.

> I had no control over what happened next. Nurse
> Rafferty opened the stretcher and my two legs swung
> out and I stood up straight. I wasn't even a bit stiff
> after all those years, and Sister Antonio noticed that I
> was holding my head myself without the collar and that
> I was using my arms and hands and that my speech was
> perfect. But when I stood up at Knock it had nothing to
> do with walking or moving. I was so full of joy and
> peace and love that has no end. It was like looking
> directly into the sun and the rays came towards me and
> I got all the gifts of that joy – the great peace and great
> love.

After thirteen years of serious disability, Marion Carroll could walk again and is said not to have suffered an ache or pain since. MS sufferers do experience periods of remission but the complete disappearance of all symptoms is highly unusual and rarely lasts for more than six years. Her case is now being studied by Dr Diarmuid Murray, who heads the Medical Bureau attached to Knock, and only after he and his colleagues satisfy themselves that she really did have MS and is now totally cured will they be prepared to apply the word 'miracle' to Marion Carroll's transformation.

Grandmother runs from shrine

Another shrine to which healing powers have been described, can be found south of Rome where Mary Goretti, an eleven-year-old girl, was fatally stabbed in 1902 by a paedophile. She forgave her killer as she lay dying and she was canonised by Pope Pius XII in 1950. When Maria Zammit, a 67-year-old British grandmother suffering from osteo-arthritis, joined fellow parishioners from a London Catholic church on a pilgrimage to St Mary Goretti's shrine in 1997, she had to use a walking stick for support. But she came out running, after undergoing an amazing transformation.

In April 1998, six months later, she was still walking without sticks and was free from pain. A devout Roman Catholic, she told the *Daily Mail* that, while she and her husband Tony, a retired fireman, were in the church, she felt a peculiar sensation. She had the urge to kneel down, but didn't do so because she thought she would not be able to get up again. 'It has been thirty years since I knelt down,' she explained. Instead she carried on praying – for her grandchildren.

'But then I felt someone say, "Aren't you going to pray for yourself?" At that moment I felt a certain looseness in my back [which] had been very painful up to that time. It had been so stiff that I could barely make the sign of the cross.'

When it came to taking communion she decided she no longer needed her stick and she went up to receive the sacrament unaided. 'I was so amazed that I began to walk around the room. When I came back to my place, I knelt down and kissed the floor. It was incredible.'

Soon she was jumping up and down to demonstrate the change in her condition, then she ran down the stairs to join her friends who were having a picnic outside. Her doctor, Justin Hayes, was initially sceptical but confirms that when she returned from Italy 'it was obvious as she walked into the room that she was experiencing much less pain and stiffness.' Her case is now being investigated by the Vatican's Congregation for Saints' Causes.

Healed by a religious relic

Throughout the Christian Church's history there have been remarkable healers, though their methods have varied greatly. The early practitioners used oil to anoint the sufferer's body but this was later replaced by holy water.

Handkerchiefs and aprons said to have belonged to St Paul were among the religious relics held against the bodies of sufferers in order to restore their failing health.

One of those who benefited from such treatment was Marguerite Perier, a novice nun who was also the niece of French philosopher and mathematician Blaise Pascal. For three years she had suffered from a fistula in her eye. Then, on 25 March 1646, she approached the altar rails and knelt before what was believed to be a thorn taken from Jesus' Crown of Thomas. Looking at the girl's terrible condition, the nun in charge suddenly picked up the thorn and touched the sore with the ancient relic. Within fifteen minutes the pus had stopped running, the ulcer had dried up and Marguerite Perier was cured of her dreadful disfigurement. So impressed was Pascal by this healing that he added an eye surrounded by a crown of thorns to his coat of arms, together with the Latin motto *Scio cui credidi*: 'What I once believed, I now know.'

However, not all visits to shrines are beneficial. *The Lancet* reported in November 1997 that a nineteen-year-old girl who drank 'holy water' from a spring developed a rash of dry, scaly patches on her skin. The condition cleared up when she stopped drinking the water and returned when she resumed drinking it. Analysis of the water showed it contained high levels of lithium, a naturally occurring metal which can aggravate psoriasis.

Blind man became Archbishop's official healer

Though shrines and holy water attract the sick and suffering in their thousands, there are those in the Church who are aware that similar, startling changes in the health of some individuals can be achieved anywhere, at any time, simply by the laying-on-of-hands. Today, throughout the Christian world, churches offer healing services to which the sick and suffering can turn when more orthodox treatments have failed to bring about an improvement. The clergy who perform such services usually make no claim to possess special powers: they simply call upon God or Jesus to bestow good health on those who seek their help. But even within the Church it is recognised that there are certain individuals through whom the healing force seems to manifest more strongly than others.

One such person was undoubtedly Godfrey Mowatt, the son of Sir Francis Mowatt, a British Government civil servant who eventually became Permanent Secretary of the Treasury. What makes him unusual in the annals of healing is that he started treating the sick very late in life and still managed to find time for many other pursuits and duties, despite himself suffering from a major handicap – blindness.

Mowatt, who was born in 1874, blinded himself accidentally at the age of seven when a penknife he was using to cut a piece of string suddenly flashed up into his left eye. Both eyes became swollen and there was nothing the doctor could do to save his sight. The sympathetic nerve in his right eye was soon affected, leaving him with 'only a glimmering' of sight in the eye he had stabbed. With remarkable determination, young Mowatt overcame the handicap and went on to marry. At about that time he had another accident. While playfully flicking a whip, its tip caught his eye 'and performed an operation of the greatest delicacy in lifting a film from it'. He was able to see his wife for the first time and for a year enjoyed the freedom which sight brought him.

However, his blindness gradually returned, though not before the birth of their only child. Much else happened in his life which caused him anguish, despair and depression, until his wife and friends formed a prayer circle to support him in their south-west London home. In time, as he improved, he began calling on others who were sick. To his surprise, he discovered that not only were they cheered by his visits but many of them reported great improvements in their physical health. Some doctors noticed that Mowatt's visits to sick people often coincided with them making a remarkable recovery, and so they began sending difficult patients to him.

All this activity came to a head in March 1919 when Mowatt had a vision in which he heard the command, 'Go forth and serve your fellow men.' But it was not until 1936, at the age of sixty-two, that he decided to dedicate the rest of his life to using his 'gift of grace' in the service of humanity. And he continued to heal the sick almost to the day he died at the age of eighty-four, in 1958.

In the meantime, Archbishop William Temple – who was Archbishop of Canterbury from 1942 to 1944 – made his own investigation of Mowatt's healing powers before making him a remarkable offer. He invited the gifted layman to Lambeth Palace where he asked if he would become his official healer. Mowatt accepted and a short service was held in the chapel at which the Archbishop placed his hands on the healer's head and said, 'Go forth, and in the power of God bring healing to the minds and bodies and to the souls of men'. In endorsing Mowatt, he hoped to bring the ministry of spiritual healing back to the position it had enjoyed in the Church's earlier days.

The story of this impressive healer is told in Kathleen Lonsdale's *Forth in Thy Name: The Life and Work of Godfrey Mowatt* (now out of print). Lonsdale, who was appointed by Archbishop Temple as the first secretary of the Churches' Council of Healing, had known Mowatt for many years and collected numerous testimonials from grateful patients.

More recently, a new audience has learned of Mowatt's extraordinary powers through Tom Harpur's superb investigation of spiritual healing, *The Uncommon Touch*. A former Anglican parish priest who moved to Canada and became a journalist who is recognised as that country's pre-eminent writer on religion and ethics, Harpur himself practised laying-on-of-hands in his days as a clergyman. It was while talking to other churchmen that he learned of Mowatt's healing ministry and uncovered some of the cases which Lonsdale had preserved. For example, during a tea break after one healing service a woman introduced herself to Mowatt and he shook her hand. She suddenly burst into tears when she realised that she had used her paralysed arm for the first time in many years.

Another woman, suffering from palsy, was in the depths of despair and had twice tried to commit suicide. Mowatt believed that an inner healing had to take place before physical healing could be achieved and over a period of time he encouraged the woman not only to put her own suffering into perspective but also to seek to help others. She lost her self-pity and her ill-health and wrote to him: 'I am digging in the garden and singing along with the birds – the happiest woman in the world.'

One of those who gave Harpur his own personal testimony was Dr Roland K. Harrison who, until his death in 1993, was editor-in-chief of the *New International Commentary on the Old Testament*. He had seen Mowatt conducting a healing service in Warrington in 1943 and, though he was not sick, he decided to go to the altar and receive the laying-on-of-hands along with dozens of others. 'I thought to myself, "I'm in good health, but since I'm about to be ordained, and on the principle that I need all the blessing I can get, I'm going to go up as well."' This is how he described to Harpur what happened next:

> The moment I felt Mowatt's hands there was a
> sensation like a weak electrical current flowing down
> my neck and spine. It remained like that for a few
> seconds until he lifted his hands from my head. It was
> really a terrific experience of a kind I had never had
> before nor have had since. The surge of 'current' felt
> slightly warm and left me with a sort of inner glow for
> a long time afterwards.

Just a few days after that conversation with Dr Harrison, Harpur was dining in a college refectory with students and a guest, the Rev. Dr Fred Crabb, who was then principal of Emmanuel College, an Anglican seminary in Saskatoon. In the course of conversation, Harpur mentioned the booklet he had recently read about Mowatt. To his astonishment, Crabb responded immediately by saying that if it had not been for Mowatt, 'I probably wouldn't be here today.' He went on to tell of a time in his life when he was suffering from a tropical disease and given six months to live. A colleague, Douglas Webster, who later became Canon and Chancellor of St Paul's Cathedral, suggested that Crabb attend a Mowatt healing service in north London. He did so, somewhat sceptically, and nothing that happened to him during the healing changed his view. 'The service of Holy Communion, taken by the vicar, was reverent and traditional,' he told Harpur:

> But – why, I still don't know – my whole soul cried out in total protest when the elderly, white-haired old gentleman moved along the row of kneeling communicants, laying his hands, as they were guided by the vicar, on the head of each worshipper, including mine. I felt no exultation, no impact of virtue or spiritual power, no difference – nothing!

But within days he began to notice a gradual improvement in his condition which continued. 'And indeed it was a long time before I admitted even to myself that, in spite of my lack of faith, God's healing grace had been at work in me because of the ministry of this very ordinary and yet singularly extraordinary old blind man, Godfrey Mowatt.'

There is just one more point worth making about the dedicated and modest Mowatt: he never took any payment for any of his healing work.

Beware frauds and charlatans

This is a far cry from some of the excesses that occur today in the name of the Lord. Encouraged by the power of television, some tele-evangelists and healer-preachers seem more concerned about attracting vast wealth than about helping the sick. Their activities are a warning to all of us that our eagerness to be whole should not cloud our common sense when seeking help from any healer.

Not all those with national or international healing ministries are frauds and charlatans, but there is enough evidence against many of them, particularly in America, for me to feel quite justified in describing what they do as theatrical clap-trap. Some descend to unimaginable depths, using spiritual blackmail to attract funds to their campaigns. Worse still are those who use trickery to convince their congregations and millions of television viewers that they possess healing and psychic powers.

One of the most brazen examples of this was Peter Popoff who ran a religious television empire across the USA and Canada from his California base. A well-known sceptical investigator of the paranormal, James Randi was sure that Popoff was faking the miracles that occurred during his cru-sades and thought he knew how it was done. Popoff would run up and down the aisles during his live services, claiming that he had 'the gift of knowledge' and calling out people's names. He would proceed to give these individuals detailed accounts of their conditions and other facts before healing them. Randi discovered that Popoff's wife, Elizabeth, was interviewing people in the foyer before the start of these meetings and then transmitting the information by radio to a small receiver in her husband's ear. Not only that, but Randi was able to record these communications and the scam was broadcast on the *Johnny Carson Show*. The TV healer's income, put at 1.25 million dollars a month before the expo-sure, took a dive once the *Carson* show went out. But he has since bounced back and his healing crusades continue to be screened in many major North American cities.

The activities of Popoff and others are enough to persuade Randi and his fellow sceptics that all healing is a sham. But there are charlatans in almost every field, and there is no rea-son why the majority of healers should be discredited by the activities of a few. It is also unfortunate that the Christian Church, in particular, should be tainted by such activities since, for every charlatan, there are perhaps one thousand healing ministries attached to churches which provide prayer and the laying on of hands without the histrionics of the tele-vision healers. Their work goes largely unsung, though some of them – such as the healing centre in the crypt of St

Marylebone Church, London, have become high-profile focal points for those eager for a greater understanding of healing.

Author Tom Harpur also believes that healing 'both as a metaphor and as a reality, might well hold the key to the renewal of religion and, more importantly, of spirituality, in the post-Christian world of the future'.

One of the better known Christian healers of recent years was John Wimber, a colourful and controversial American who was a keyboard player with the Righteous Brothers before becoming an evangelist, healer and founder of the Association of Vineyard Churches which has 450 congregations in the US and 250 more in forty-seven other countries. His services were characterised by strange behaviour. People wept, laughed, ran about, barked like dogs, had apparent convulsions and did all manner of other things during his ministries. Such activities naturally had their detractors but an English anthropologist decided to make a comprehensive analysis of the healings which took place at a John Wimber conference held in Harrogate, Yorkshire, in the autumn of 1986, attended by nearly 2500 people from various Christian denominations. Though a Christian himself, Dr David C. Lewis was also a social anthropologist in the universities of Cambridge and Manchester, and he therefore produced a fairly detached assessment of the remarkable happenings.

Dr Lewis, who published his findings in 1989 in *Healing: Fiction, Fantasy or Fact?* received 1890 completed questionnaires after the conference in which the participants gave detailed replies to a wide range of questions about themselves, the phenomena they had witnessed and any healing they had received. He then followed up 100 of these, chosen at random, six months to a year later by conducting in-depth, personal interviews. Having collected his data, Dr Lewis used a computerised analytical model to study the findings.

The result is the most thorough study of a healing conference ever undertaken. He was able to confirm that many remarkable healings did take place. The purpose of the conference was to train 'novice healers', many of those attending therefore had no need of healing for themselves. But 621 who completed the questionnaire said they had sought healing help, and of these 68 claimed to have been totally healed by the prayers said on their behalf. The others reported different degrees of success, including some who showed no benefit.

John Wimber's healing ministry came to an end in November 1997 when he died, either after a brain haemorrhage following triple heart surgery, or after a fall, depending on which story one believes. His death, it seems, was as controversial as some aspects of his life.

Putting prayer to the test

The first double-blind prayer experiment was conducted at the London Hospital Medical College in the early 1960s by psychopharmacologist Dr C.R.B. Joyce in collaboration with R.M.C. Welldon. They found several pairs of patients whose age, sex and clinical diagnosis (they were suffering either from rheumatoid arthritis or psychological disorders) matched. But only one member of each pair was prayed for by specially chosen groups. The patients, of course, were not given details of the study, and their doctors – totally unaware of how the experiment was being conducted – were simply asked to report periodically on their patients' condition, rating improvement by using a numerical scale.

The pioneering prayer project was not a success. Although initial results seemed to indicate that the patients being prayed for were making far better progress than those who had been ignored, the longer the experiment was conducted, the more the reverse seemed to be true. The project eventually came to an end on a note of uncertainty. One obvious conclusion, which sceptics will prefer, is that it demonstrated that prayer does not work. But the researchers have been criticised for the instructions they gave to the prayer groups. Joyce and Welldon told them to use a form of silent Christian prayer or meditation in which they first had to still their thoughts and focus their attention on a selected quotation from the Bible. Then, while expressing this positive affirmation of God, they were told to build up with their prayers a mental image of the experimental patient and his or her name. It seems, however, that they were not told to make a specific petition for the patient's recovery. We know that healers use many different methods, so perhaps these instructions were too much of a spiritual straitjacket for the groups' prayers to express themselves adequately.

However, the efforts of the London pair encouraged American researcher Dr Platon J. Collipp to try to replicate their study in 1969. Collipp was chairman of the Paediatrics Department of Meadowbrook Hospital, New York, when he decided to try a more straightforward test. He chose only one disease, childhood leukaemia, with a known and, at that time, usually fatal prognosis and arranged for several physicians to supply him with the names, ages and dates of diagnoses for eighteen children afflicted with the disease, all of whom were receiving similar forms of chemotherapy. Incidentally, none of the doctors nor their patients knew that they were taking part in a study on the power of prayer.

Collipp then identified ten family prayer groups in Washington State who were given the names of ten of the children and asked to pray for them. The names of the other eight children were not given to the prayer groups. At the end of the project, fifteen months later, the results were fairly conclusive. Eight of the ten children for whom prayers had been said were still alive, whereas only two of the eight 'control' children, whose names were not on the list, had survived.

After all the scientific research there is a question that still needs to be answered. Are the dramatic cures reported from around the world – whether ascribed to prayer or other forms of healing – evidence of an outside healing power at work in our lives, or *just* the products of our own minds, whose incredible powers are perhaps far greater than we suspect?

A *wish granted through prayer*

A number of charities have been established to help make the wishes of dying children come true. One of these is the

Make-a-Wish Foundation which arranged for seventeen-year-old American leukaemia victim Amy Graham to attend a seminar run by the Rev. Mark Victor Hansen. She knew she had only days to live. He tells her story in his book *Chicken Soup for the Soul*. Amy was one of a thousand attendees, but she made an impression on Hansen when she and her parents met him during the morning session.

As the day progressed, Hansen asked his audience if they would like to learn a healing technique. They readily agreed and he demonstrated how they should rub their hands together vigorously, then separate them by 2 inches (5 cm) and feel the healing energy. Then he said to them: 'This morning I was introduced to Amy Graham, a seventeen-year-old, whose final wish was to be at this seminar. I want to bring her up here and let you all send healing life-force energy toward her. Perhaps we can help. She did not request it. I am just doing this spontaneously because it feels right.'

Amy's father led her onto the platform. The effects of chemotherapy, lack of exercise and too much bed rest were all too evident. Hansen asked the audience to repeat the healing technique he had shown them and direct the energy to Amy. They then gave her a tearful standing ovation.

'Two weeks later,' he writes, 'she called to say that her doctor had discharged her after a total remission. Two years later she called to say she had married.'

The power of prayer must not be judged on a single case, of course. But cardiologist Dr Randolph Byrd, a former professor at the University of California, has provided us with quantitative evidence not only that prayer really does work but that it can play an important role in healing. In the 1980s, he took 393 patients in a San Francisco coronary care unit and divided them into two matched groups. Half the patients were prayed for by an outside group of 'born-again' Christians; and half were not. Neither the patients nor their carers knew which patients were being prayed for.

Over a ten-month period, Byrd carefully recorded any complications that befell the two sets of patients during hospitalisation, including their need for drugs, medical treatment and operations. When the results were evaluated, it was found that 84 per cent of the prayed-for group was judged to have had a 'good' hospital stay, as opposed to only 73 per cent of the control group. The difference between the two sets of results may not seem impressive to a layman, but a scientist would readily agree that they were statistically very significant. Indeed, it has been argued that, had a drug or clinical procedure been involved, rather than prayer or healing, it would have been claimed as a major medical breakthrough. He presented his findings to the American Heart Association's meeting in Miami, Florida, in 1985.

'Based on this study I believe prayer is effective and beneficial,' Dr Byrd told the *Medical Tribune*, which reported the research in January 1986. 'This study gives scientific evidence to something Christians have believed for years – that God answers.' Even a well-known sceptic like Dr William Nolen of Litchfield, Minnesota, author of *Healing: A Doctor in Search of a Miracle*, admitted: 'It sounds like this study will stand up to scrutiny.' And he told the *Chicago Sun-Times* that perhaps doctors should in future prescribe prayers 'three times a day' along with their patients' regular treatment.

4

ALL IN THE MIND?

Before we attribute such cures to a powerful, invisible healing force, we need to consider a simpler solution. Could it be that healing comes from within? Is it possible that we all have the power to heal ourselves?

Most of us tend to think that our health is beyond our control. When we become sick we rely on a vast range of drugs and other treatments to make us better. And if they fail, in desperation we turn to healers and alternative practitioners. However, some would argue that they only succeed by making us believe that they can cure our ailments . . . and our minds do the rest.

The evidence that the mind is a powerful healer is beyond question. In fact, the only mystery is why science and medicine have not done more to find out about mental power and teach us how to harness it.

Mesmer's 'animal magnetism'

One of the first people to demonstrate the mind's curative powers, as well as some of its other astonishing abilities, was an eighteenth-century Austrian physician, Franz Anton Mesmer. He believed his discovery (called 'animal magnetism'), which induced a trance-like state in his patients, was the result of the transfer of magnetism from him or his 'magnetised' equipment to the individuals seeking his help. These magnetic treatments, he maintained, restored the patients' health and 'bodily balance'. Mesmer's Austrian colleagues largely frowned on his claims, but the witty and charming physician had many followers in his home country and went on to enjoy even greater popularity in France where his patients included Marie Antoinette, wife of King Louis XVI.

But the impact of Mesmer's controversial healing techniques led the king to appoint a royal commission to investigate his claims in March 1784. Benjamin Franklin, the 78-year-old American Ambassador to France, was chosen to be its head, and the other members included the father of modern chemistry, Dr Antoine-Laurent Lavoisier, and physician Joseph-Ignace Guillotin, whose very clever invention was later used to behead the royal couple. The commission interviewed many who had been helped by Mesmer's techniques and witnessed their effects which, they testified, included convulsions, piercing cries, tears, hiccoughs and extravagant laughter. Despite all the evidence, the French King's commission was unimpressed. It found no evidence of magnetism in any of the paraphernalia Mesmer used in his treatments and it dismissed the reported cures as imagination.

There was one dissenting voice, that of botanist Dr Antoine Laurent de Jussieu, who issued a minority report saying he was satisfied that Mesmer's induction of trance *had* produced inexplicable cures, even though it may have done so simply by mobilising the patient's imagination. This was a view with which Benjamin Franklin seems to have agreed, even though, as commission chairman, he signed the damning report. The damage done, Mesmer's career as a healer quickly declined, though his memory lives on in two English words, 'mesmerism' and 'mesmerise', though mesmerism is better known today as 'hypnotism'.

Mesmerism as an anaesthetic

There were other medical pioneers, however, who were prepared to continue Mesmer's work, braving the contempt of their colleagues. Among them was John Elliotson, a founder of London's University College Hospital, which was the first to establish an association with a medical college so that students were able to carry out clinical research. Having witnessed a demonstration of mesmerism in France in 1837, Elliotson immediately realised its potential as a means of controlling surgical pain. He learned to mesmerise his own patients and was soon performing amputations of legs, arms and breasts without any anaesthetic. Yet his more narrow-minded colleagues refused to believe the evidence of their own eyes. His patients, they maintained, had been trained not to express pain.

The use of mesmerism as a means of ridding a patient of pain during surgery was also appreciated by James Esdaile, an East India Company doctor, who read an article about the technique in the *Zoist*, which Elliotson published. Esdaile tried it first on a convict who obligingly fell into a deep trance immediately. He went on to perform thousands of surgical operations in India in the 1860s, using mesmerism to 'switch off' the body's pain sensors, and saving many lives in the process. These operations included amputations, the removal of tumours, draining abscesses and extracting teeth.

In that country, over a century ago, scrotal tumours were quite prevalent. Few surgeons were prepared to operate on the unfortunate sufferers because half of them died after surgery. However, Esdaile's mortality rate was just 5 per cent and he seems to have been prepared to take on any case, however difficult. One of the tumours he removed weighed 103lb (47 kg) and was as heavy as the patient's body. The tumour had to be supported by means of a rope and pulley in the rafters before he put the patient into a trance and separated him from the huge growth.

Many of these operations were performed while Esdaile was attached to the Native Hospital in Hooghly and the government of Bengal was so impressed with his results they put him in charge of a small hospital in Calcutta in 1846 and renamed it the Mesmeric Hospital. But others ridiculed him and he was expelled from the British Medical Society. The sceptics again argued that his patients were just pretending not to feel pain because they loved operations. Esdaile, like Mesmer himself, was seemingly unaware of the importance of the mind in these surgical interventions. He was convinced that the sleep-like state he produced in his patients was achieved by 'pouring' a healing fluid into them.

The birth of hypnotism

It was another nineteenth-century British surgeon, James Braid, who gave mesmerism a new lease of life by coining the term hypnosis (from the Greek *hypnos*, meaning 'sleep'). Manchester-born Braid used it for major surgery but failed to convince the British Medical Association, which examined the whole subject at the beginning of this century, that it had a place in modern medicine. In fact, it was not until 1958 that the American Medical Association gave official sanction to the use of hypnosis by physicians.

With the development of modern painkillers and anaesthetics, hypnotism is rarely needed in the operating theatre today, except in cases where the patient is allergic to those drugs. A 1979 review of medical literature discovered just two dozen such cases over the previous twenty years. They included an appendectomy, a Caesarean section and several kinds of heart surgery. The *American Journal of Clinical Hypnosis* has carried a report by an Ontario dentist, Victor Rausch, who routinely uses hypnosis in his practice. When he needed gall bladder surgery, Rausch refused conventional anaesthetics and instead hypnotised himself. The doctors cut him open, removed his gall bladder, then sewed up the wound. The surgery complete, Rausch calmly rose from the operating table and walked back to his room.

Relaxing into health

Such dramatic demonstrations of the mind's control over the body are rare, but hundreds of thousands of people around the world put time aside every day to perform various mental relaxation techniques. Whether it is yoga, transcendental meditation, visualisation or some other form of focusing of the mind is perhaps unimportant. What matters is that they have discovered the need to cultivate a better mind-body relationship and have learned techniques which accomplish this and are suited to their temperament.

They all report very similar feelings of relaxation and that is bound to produce health benefits. Medical tests have confirmed that during such mental exercises there is a noticeable drop in blood pressure. A group of patients with heart problems who were taught relaxation techniques displayed improvements in cardiovascular health over several years, compared with a control group. Indeed, numerous studies have chronicled a whole range of improvements that derive from relaxation – from easing of irritable bowel syndrome symptoms to the lessening of severe pain. Meditation seems to achieve its healing results in part by stilling the mind and ridding the body of the stress which is a major cause of disease.

How does it do this? How can the mind 'talk' to the body and produce the desired results? And how does a healing force communicate its intention to the patient to bring about an improvement?

The answer, say many psychically gifted healers, is to be found in the aura – a colourful, luminous emanation which they can see around a person, particularly around the head, and which is believed to be related to our electromagnetic field. The dominant colour tells the healer about the person's mood, thoughts and state of physical health.

Auras and Chakras

I have never seen an aura, but I have felt one! It happened some years ago when I attended a social gathering to which several mediums had been invited. During a conversation with Bill Mayer, an east London healer, he pointed to an elderly lady seated on the other side of the room and, without explanation, insisted that I went to speak to her. I did so, and in order to introduce myself and make myself heard in a very noisy room I had to bend close to her. As I did so, I experienced an incredible sensation, unlike anything I had felt before, or since. My face felt as if it was being pricked by sharp-pointed instruments: it was similar to the 'pins and needles' feeling you get in a limb when the blood supply is cut off.

Our chat was brief and trivial, partly because my mind was more occupied with the strange feeling than with what we were talking about. Had I eaten or drunk something that disagreed with me? Was I about to faint? I made my excuses and returned to Bill Mayer, and the sensation immediately left me.

'Did you feel it?' he asked.

'Feel what?' I responded defensively.

'The power! Many people feel it when they get close to her. I've felt it myself. It's like pins and needles.'

Only then did I tell him what I had felt, and I was grateful that he had not told me what to expect or I would probably have dismissed it as my imagination. As a result of that experience, I have no doubt that the very tangible energy I felt is what becomes visible as the aura to some psychics. It is defined by aura reader Rosalyn L. Bruyere as 'a luminous radiation, a field of light or energy that extends beyond the body to interact with our external environment. It is an energy system that keeps body and mind alive and healthy, and may in actuality create them.'

She has been able to see auras from an early age and explains that this field of energy usually extends 5 or 6 inches (12–15 cm) around the body. The aura itself, she adds, is generated by the spinning of smaller vortices of energy – chakras – located within the body, of which seven are known as the principal chakras. These run from the top of the head to the base of the spine and, tradition tells us, each one is associated with a particular gland and has a distinct colour, purpose and physical and spiritual associations. What goes on in our minds or bodies affects our chakras and this in turn is reflected in our aura. So our auric colours for example, may tell a psychic which chakra is being affected by particular emotions. By the same token, receiving healing or going into an altered state of mind, such as during meditation or hypnosis, may enable us to bring about changes in our chakras which then produce physical or mental improvements. But talking about the mind affecting physical health may be too simplistic.

'In fact,' says Rosalyn Bruyere, 'some scientists believe from their studies that the mind is not in the brain but in the body's energy field, and that the mind, chakras and aura are all connected.'

What happens when healing takes place, she believes, is that a healer transmits energy into the patient and, having detected a particular deficiency in a chakra, channels his or her own chakra energy into the corresponding chakra of the person being treated.

Damaged bone is made to grow

In his book *The Power of the Mind*, one of Britain's most experienced hypnotists, Joe Keeton, quotes numerous cases in which individuals have overcome serious health conditions as a result of hypnosis. They include a startling case in which a young woman, whose heel bone was shattered in a motorbike accident, and who at one point faced the possibility of amputation, made a remarkable recovery which appeared to include new growth of the damaged bone. Her doctor testified that hypnosis was an extremely valuable psychological aid in her recovery 'and the improvement which occurred in the condition of her heel was much greater than any of her medical advisers anticipated'. He added: 'I can offer no incontrovertible proof that the hypnosis did provide growth stimulus, but I am convinced in my own mind that it did affect the healing process.'

Mind control: a burning issue

It is obvious that our minds have a direct and easily demonstrable influence on our skin – the body's largest organ. If we get embarrassed we blush, and we sometimes turn red with anger. However, the extraordinary closeness of the links between the mind and our body's covering was not fully accepted until the 1960s when the *American Journal of Clinical Hypnosis* carried a report that has come to be known as 'The Case of the Sunless Sunburn'.

A young woman, who had been hypnotised by her psychotherapist, was told to relax. To help her achieve that state, he suggested she imagined she was on a sunny beach. Almost at once she cried out, 'I feel like I'm on fire', and he watched in astonishment as an angry rash rapidly developed on her face, shoulders and upper arms. It was eighteen hours before this skin condition disappeared, by which time the psychotherapist had discovered that the woman had once suffered exactly the same reaction, perhaps due to a drug she was taking at that time, when she stepped onto a real beach.

Other hypnotists have reported the sudden appearance on patients' bodies of burns and wounds corresponding to those they have suffered in earlier traumatic episodes and which they subsequently recall. Nor does it require a real event to produce such an effect. If an ordinary coin is placed on a hypnotised patient's arm and that person is told it is red hot, a blister is likely to form. The mind is an incredibly powerful instrument, and an estimated 15 per cent of people are highly suggestible, making them good hypnotic subjects.

If a cool coin can 'burn' a person in a trance, then perhaps the reverse is also true. Could hypnotism be used to reduce the pain and suffering of burns victims? Dr Dabney Ewin of Tulane University, New Orleans, where he is an associate professor of surgery, began experimenting with this idea in the 1970s and was soon recording remarkable results. For example, when a worker fell into 950°C molten lead up to his knees, he was rushed to Dr Ewin who knew the man to be a good hypnotic subject. He should have suffered third-degree burns requiring skin grafts and a lengthy stay in hospital. Instead, only second-degree burns occurred and he was out of hospital in three weeks.

In another case, a patient's arm was badly damaged by an

explosion of acetylene, which burns at 3000°C. Dr Ewin was able to hypnotise him within an hour, implanting the suggestion that the arm felt cool and comfortable, before dressing the wound and sending him back to work. Next day, when he checked the man's condition, the skin was still charred but there was no swelling, infection or pain. Within twelve days the arm was completely healed.

'If you can get to them within the first two hours, before the response has been released, you can block the response and, in effect, have them react as though they had not been burned,' Dr Ewin explains.

Sceptics tempted to dismiss such claims as anecdotal should also consider the findings of Drs Jerold Kaplan and Lawrence Moore at the Alta Bates Hospital burns unit, in Berkeley, California. They selected five patients who had been burned equally on both sides of their bodies. Then, using hypnotism, they directed healing suggestions to just one side. In four of the five patients, healing was more advanced in the areas to which hypnotic suggestion was directed.

Incurable skin condition clears up

Of all skin conditions, warts are known to be the most responsive to hypnotic suggestion. There are countless medical reports recording the rapid disappearance of clusters of unsightly warts, which are caused by a virus. So, when anaesthetist Dr Albert A. Mason, a senior registrar at the Queen Victoria Hospital, East Grinstead, Sussex, who was also a skilled hypnotist, was told that a sixteen-year-old boy with 'large warty excrescences' ¼ inch (5 mm) wide all over his legs and feet, was incurable, he thought he knew better. Plastic surgery had been tried on his hands, which had been covered in a 'rigid, horny casing'. This was scraped off in the operating theatre in 1950 and skin transplants used to replace it, but within a month the new skin also hardened and turned black.

Mason was then allowed by his sceptical colleagues to try hypnotism. He explained to the entranced boy that the warts were going to fall off his left arm, and asked him to return a week later. When he did so, Mason was delighted to learn that after five days the horny layer of skin had softened, become friable and then fallen off, leaving what appeared to be normal skin underneath. After another five days his arm was completely clear from shoulder to wrist. There had been no change to the skin on other parts of his body.

'Well,' he said, as he took the boy in to see the hospital's leading surgeon. 'I told you warts did very well with hypnosis.'

'Jesus Christ!' the surgeon exclaimed on examining the boy. 'Do you know what you've done? This is a case of congenital ichthyosiform erythrodermia of Brocq. Now go into the library and look it up.'

Mason did so, discovering not only that ichthyosis – known as 'fish skin disease' – is a congenital condition but also structural and organic. That meant, he realised, that the patient's skin had no oil-forming glands that could cause its outer layers to flake off and renew themselves. The black, evil-smelling, bacteria-ridden armour-plating would just go on building up. Yet not only was his left arm largely clear of the condition, but Mason also went on to achieve an impressive improvement in other areas of his body over the next few weeks. The scales fell off the other arm, from the palms of his hands, from 90 per cent of his back, and from 50 to 70 per cent of his legs and buttocks. When reported in the columns of the *British Medical Journal* it created a sensation.

Within a year the boy had got a job as an electrician's assistant and, three years later, Mason was delighted to discover that the improvement had been maintained. He decided to offer further hypnotic sessions to try to clear up the remaining areas of scaly skin and the young man agreed. Yet, to Mason's astonishment, he found he was now 'totally unhypnotisable'.

In 1961 Mason revealed another surprise, again in the pages of the *British Medical Journal*. After his success with the boy, he reported, he had tackled another eight cases of congenital ichthyosis. Every one had been a complete failure. But in the same year, Dr C.A.S. Wink, an Oxford general practitioner, reported that he had used hypnotism successfully to treat two sisters, aged seven and five. Like Mason, he had worked on one part of the body at a time. And, though there had been a vast improvement, the condition had not cleared totally in either child.

Discussing these cases, Guy Lyon Playfair asks a number of pertinent questions in *If this Be Magic*:

Why should a hypnotist succeed with one patient, then fail with eight others? Why should he be unable to hypnotise his original patient four years later? Why should Wink succeed with *two* patients? Why should some parts of the body respond to suggestion under hypnosis more than others? Above all, why on earth should any part of the body respond at all? As Mason himself put it, referring to ichthyosis and a couple of other skin diseases that he had managed to treat successfully: 'When one considers that these conditions are caused by a congenital *absence* of certain dermal tissues, one can only conjecture wildly as to why they should respond to anything'.

It seems that there is more involved than just the *patients'* minds. When Mason took on the case he assumed he was dealing with a severe case of curable warts and his expectation of success must have been conveyed to his young patient. By the time he tackled the other eight cases, he knew he was dealing with an 'incurable' disease. His own inability to comprehend how the mind could repair the body in those circumstances may therefore have conveyed itself to his new patients, and may also have been a factor in him no longer being able to hypnotise his first patient. Finally, suggests Playfair, Wink had read Mason's first report and so he was embarking on the treatment with the two sisters in the knowledge that the disease was largely curable by hypnosis – and so he achieved positive results.

Warts melt away

According to Dr Andrew Weil in his book *Health and Healing*, all conventional medical treatments had failed to help a man in his fifties who had suffered for years from warts covering most of his body. Finally his physician told him there was a new, powerful but potentially dangerous form of X-ray treatment that might help. The man undressed and stood in the darkened room as the X-ray machine hummed impressively. In fact it did not emit a single ray but it was sufficient that the patient believed he was receiving a special treatment. Next day, all the warts had melted away.

Hypnotism, then, is not essential for the mind to produce healing miracles or changes in its physical condition. Strong belief, it seems, is enough in itself.

In fact, without realising it, we all slip into different states of consciousness almost every day. Watching a compelling film or television programme, for example, can induce such a heightened state of concentration that we might be oblivious to events going on around us. At times we may realise that we have been so deep in thought that we have been on 'automatic pilot' while driving a vehicle, and have no conscious memory of the passing scenery. It is totally wrong, therefore, to regard a hypnotised person as 'asleep'. In reality, he or she is in a state of concentrated, focused relaxation.

Media message muddled his mind

The same might be true of people who have a strong belief that something is going to happen to them. A cancer patient, who has been given the pseudonym Mr Wright, figures prominently in medical literature for precisely this reason. This is an extraordinary story that demonstrates better than most the incredible power of the mind. Wright, a patient of Drs Philip West and Bruno Klopfer in the 1950s, was dying from cancer of the lymph nodes which had produced orange-sized tumours in his neck, under his arms and in his groin, chest and abdomen. He needed oxygen, was running a fever and was regarded by his doctors as 'in a terminal state', 'untreatable' except for sedatives 'to ease him on his way'.

Then Wright heard about a new wonder drug, Krebiozen, and though he was too sick to warrant its use, West and Klopfer gave in to his pleading. His first dose made him so sick that they thought it would be his last. But three days later, Dr West found the patient 'walking around the ward, chatting happily with the nurses, and spreading his message of good cheer to anyone who would listen.' When he examined Wright he discovered that 'the tumour masses had melted away like snowballs on a hot stove, and in only these few days, they were half their original size.' Within ten days, they discharged Wright from the hospital. His cancer had virtually vanished.

That would have been the perfect ending to the story, but the power of his mind was about to unfold a different drama. Soon, Wright read newspaper reports that the experimental wonder drug Krebiozen had not lived up to expectations and few patients had improved after taking it. He took the news badly. After just two months of good health, Wright was back in hospital. Dr West, aware that the patient's mental state appeared to have played a major role in his earlier recovery, decided to try an experiment. He reassured Wright about Krebiozen and told him a shipment of 'super-refined, double-strength' Krebiozen was on its way. 'By delaying a couple of days before the "shipment" arrived,' West wrote, 'his anticipation of salvation had reached a tremendous pitch. When I announced that the new series of injections was about to begin, he was almost ecstatic and his faith was very strong.'

In fact, Wright's recovery was even more dramatic than the first time. The tumours diminished and he was soon 'the picture of health' and returned to a normal life. What he did not know, however, was that the second series of injections were not of Krebiozen at all but of sterile water. They had proved the power of Wright's mind to be strong enough to overcome his advanced cancer. Unfortunately, the power of his mind was eventually to be his undoing. Not long after his recovery, the American Medical Association made a formal announcement that 'nationwide tests show Krebiozen to be a worthless drug for the treatment of cancer.' Within days, the dejected and dispirited Wright went into hospital and quickly died.

Mystery of placebos

What Mr Wright experienced is well known to Western science. It is called the placebo effect. But this term can cause some confusion. Governments require new drugs to be thoroughly tested before they are made freely available and the usual way of doing this is to conduct controlled trials in which some sufferers are given the new drug while others are given 'sugar pills' or some similar, innocuous placebo, so that doctors can compare the benefits of the former with the latter. Such experiments usually work to everyone's satisfaction, but the focus of attention, naturally, is on the new drug. Little research has been done to explain the fact that some patients receiving only sugar pills also show improvement.

In 1955, physician Henry Beecher of Harvard reviewed fifteen double-blind studies in which patients were given placebos to treat a variety of conditions, including headache, seasickness, anxiety, pain and the common cold. In one third of cases, the placebos removed their symptoms, suggesting that one third of the drugs prescribed in the United States may work primarily through the placebo effect.

And it is not only placebo drugs which produce results. In the late 1950s, American surgeons developed an operation, known as angina pectoris, to relieve heart pain caused when insufficient blood reaches the heart muscle. They tried to create a detour by tying off a nearby artery, but controversy about the value of these operations soon erupted and there were conflicting reports about the degree of pain relief experienced by patients. It seemed that the more sceptical the surgeon, the lower the rate of success.

'What happened next could not happen today, with the emphasis on patients' rights and informed consent for all procedures,' says *The Heart of Healing*, published by The Institute of Noetic Sciences:

> Several surgeons decided to test the angina operation by performing placebo surgeries in which they cut open their patients and then closed them back up again without tying off the artery. These patients experienced everything the medical system could offer – the attention of their doctors, the drama of preparing for surgery, the surgical incision, nurturance during recovery, and the expectation that the new and widely hailed treatment would improve their condition – except the treatment itself. The doctors found that the phoney surgeries proved no less beneficial to patients than the real thing. In one study, *more* patients who had undergone the sham operation reported relief. Placebo surgery reduced the patients' use of nitro-glycerine, the most common pain reliever for angina. It also increased patients' capacity for exercise and the amount they could work.

But let us not fool ourselves into thinking that there are only benefits to be derived from placebo effects. Astonishingly, it seems that the mind can also trick the body into experiencing the less desirable side-effects which often accompany conventional medical treatment. These side-effects include drowsiness, nausea, diarrhoea, sleep disturbance and skin rashes. Most surprising of all, the *World Journal of Surgery* reported in 1983 on the effectiveness of various chemotherapies for certain types of cancer and their common and expected side-effects, including hair loss. Buried in these statistics was the startling revelation that nearly one third of patients given a placebo instead of chemotherapy had also lost their hair.

Until such evidence became available it was thought that the placebo effect was no more than a 'feel good' factor: that the improvement reported by patients was a psychological assessment of feeling better on their part, rather than the result of any physical changes. But various studies have recorded coughs, skin rashes, and alterations in reaction time, grip strength, pulse rate, blood pressure and stomach action which are all believed to be directly related to the taking of a placebo. Just believing that it will make them better seems to be enough for many people's bodies to start the healing process and produce physical changes.

This was confirmed in 1978 by researchers studying the way the body produces powerful pain relievers, called endorphins, which are released at times of stress to block specific pain receptors in the brain. They wondered if expectation and belief, rather than an actual event, might also trigger the release of endorphins, which would explain why the anticipated effect of a placebo drug could make it a painkiller. Their tests were carried out with dental patients in a San Francisco clinic who were suffering severe pain after the removal of impacted wisdom teeth. In randomised trials, a number of patients were given placebos instead of painkillers and 40 per cent reported significant relief from the pain. Later, they received a dose of naloxone, a drug which blocks the effects of endorphins, and almost immediately they complained that the pain was returning. So, while it is clearly a complex subject, the evidence suggests that placebos can stimulate the body's internal pain relief system . . . and probably much more besides.

More than a thinking machine

Deepak Chopra, the New England endocrinologist and New Age guru who has inspired many people to rethink the mind–body relationship, explores such issues in his book *Quantum Healing*. Using simple language, he deals with complicated discoveries in medicine, physics and metaphysics, unravelling in the process some of the mysteries of our biological processes and revealing that every cell in our body has an endless number of messages it can send and receive. Yet it is also clear that only a small fraction are activated at any one time.

'Who or what controls the messages?' Chopra asks:

That turns out to be an explosive question. In a
chemistry lab, reactions will run automatically as soon
as the experiment starts; it is just a matter of mixing
one chemical with another. Yet someone has to take the
chemicals off the shelf to begin with.

Medicine has traditionally preferred to ignore this
fact as it applies to the human body. Now we see that
with thousands of chemicals on its shelf, a cell has not
only to choose some, mix them together, and analyse
the results. It has to make the chemicals in the first
place, finding thousands of ways to create new
molecules out of basically a handful of elements –
carbon, hydrogen, oxygen and nitrogen. To do that
requires a mind. So, by following the story of
neuropeptides, we have ultimately arrived at a dramatic
shift in worldview. For the first time in the history of
science, mind has a visible scaffold to stand upon.
Before this, science declared that we are physical
machines that have somehow learned to think. Now it
dawns that we are thoughts that have learned to create
a physical machine.

In two minds?

But what about a physical machine – a human body – that is
apparently inhabited by more than one person: an individual
with so-called multiple personality disorder (MPD).
Accounts of such cases are often bizarre and beyond the com-
prehension of most people. Indeed, they are treated today by
some sceptics with as much derision as the early reports of
hypnosis. What is relevant to this discussion is the research
which has been done with MPD sufferers who also have aller-
gies. Dr Bennett Braun, founder of America's first in-patient
unit for dissociative disorders at Rush Presbyterian Hospital,
Chicago, tells of a patient who was allergic to cats in one personality and not another. He has also studied a boy who was

allergic to orange juice in all but one of his almost dozen personalities. He could drink orange juice and digest it in this personality, but if he changed too soon to any of the others, he would develop a rash, which would then disappear if he switched back to the non-allergic personality.

Our minds it seems, rule our bodies . . . or would, if we gave them half a chance. But is that the whole story? Can we assume that healing is simply due to the power of the mind, and close the book on all other explanations? Hardly. Mind power is certainly an important part of the picture, but, as we are about to see, there are still some unsolved mysteries which suggest that there may, after all, be a powerful, exterior healing force at work in the world.

5

HEALING UNDER THE MICROSCOPE

I first met Matthew Manning in the 1970s, soon after the publication of his book, *The Link*, which told the astonishing story of how he, his family and his schoolfriends were plagued by poltergeist phenomena. He was eleven years old when bizarre things started happening around him and he was still a teenager when the media picked up his story and he became a household name in many countries. The book sold over a million copies and was published in sixteen languages.

What made Manning different was that he had somehow learned to channel the poltergeist energy – which is frequently disturbing and destructive – into more constructive, if puzzling, manifestations. These included automatic writing, in which he seemed to receive written messages from someone who had lived in the Cambridgeshire home he shared with his parents, brother and sister. In fact, the walls of the study became covered in automatic signatures. And he discovered that, just by thinking of a famous artist, he could draw in their style.

All this happened when Uri Geller was making his first impact and so, when the press learned that young Manning was also claiming to be able to bend keys and spoons, they beat a path to his door. It was at this time that I interviewed him for a magazine I was editing on the paranormal. We discussed at length not only the psychic phenomena that continued to occur in his presence but also the great interest his powers had aroused. He struck me as a very down-to-earth young man, if slightly flamboyant, and – to his credit – he seemed to be taking all the adulation in his stride. He showed no concern about what might happen in the future if his powers disappeared – a likely event, I thought, since poltergeist phenomena have a habit of vanishing when the adolescent around whom they manifest becomes an adult.

Eager to be tested

My most recent meeting with Manning was at the 1997 Mind, Body, Spirit Festival in London. His spoon-bending and automatic writing days are long gone but he now has a huge following as one of Britain's leading healers. Married with two children, he remains an unconventional and outspoken figure. Nor have the passing years diminished his flamboyance, as shown by his 'trademark' brightly coloured jackets. The transition from poltergeist victim to famous healer may seem unlikely but many healers discover their powers in unusual ways – some by hearing voices, others by being guided to place their hands on the sick.

Unlike Geller, who seemed rather unwilling to work with scientists to prove his paranormal abilities, the teenage Manning had been ready – even eager – to participate in a wide range of tests in a number of countries. He refused to accept fees for this work, just his expenses. Most of the tests concerned 'mind over matter' (or psychokinesis), in which he attempted to bend metal or influence objects at a distance.

Then, in 1977, they began to follow a different pattern. He was invited to San Antonio, Texas, by a group of scientists at the Mind Science Foundation, led by Dr William Braud, who had some unusual ideas he wanted to explore with the young British psychic. Braud used to be a professor of psychology at the University of Houston, before becoming a researcher at the foundation, and is today one of the most respected figures in parapsychology. The results of these preliminary

experiments were so successful that he went back the following year for several weeks to continue the tests. They included
trying to influence the orientation of an electric-knife fish in
an aquarium, and the motor movement of a gerbil. Most of
these trials produced statistically significant results and were
published by the scientists.

'However,' Manning tells us in his book, *No Faith
Required*, 'there were two tests which provided very striking
results and which showed it was clearly possible to demonstrate healing in a laboratory.'

One of them involved human blood cells. When human
blood is mixed with water, the red blood cells become
stressed and haemoglobin escapes into the surrounding solution. The red blood cells survive intact much longer if placed
in a saline solution. Scientists can measure the haemoglobin
escape – called haemolysis – by monitoring the amount of
light transmitted through the blood–water solution, because
its appearance changes from cloudy to clear as haemolysis
occurs.

This is Manning's account of what happened when he was
asked to concentrate on trying to prevent the red blood cells
from being broken down, once they had been placed in water
with only a very small saline content:

> There was a sequence of five trials during which I was
> to exert a healing influence, and five trials during which
> for control purposes I removed my influence. The
> instructions as to what I was to do were based on the
> random order of ten cards shuffled twenty times: five of
> the cards would be blank and the other five would tell
> me to influence. During one of the trials I was placed in
> a distant room and had to influence the blood cells
> from 30 metres away. The scientists then accurately
> measured the extent to which the cells broke down by
> placing the test tubes in a machine, called a
> spectrophotometer, which measured the amount of
> light being transmitted through the solution. This time
> the results, when analysed statistically, beat chance by

odds of over 100,000 to one. Most interestingly, it was found that the one trial where I influenced the blood cells from 30 metres away produced the greatest response!

In his report, Dr Braud wrote: 'The major conclusion to be drawn from these experiments, of course, is that Matthew Manning was able to exert significant psychokinetic influence upon a variety of biological targets.'

Healing kills cancer cells

Manning also took part in another series of experiments at San Antonio, conducted by Dr John Kmetz, a physiologist, at the Science Unlimited Research Foundation, a privately funded parapsychological research laboratory. Kmetz had been doing research with cancer cells and a young American healer named Dean Kraft. Scott Rogo, one of the most level-headed chroniclers of the paranormal, tells the story of those experiments in *Psychic Breakthroughs Today*. One of Kraft's most spectacular abilities, he explains, is 'his talent for killing cancer cells grown in special culture flasks'. This ability was well documented in July 1977 when he co-operated in tests in which Dr Kmetz used 'an especially virulent form of cancer cell, the HeLa cell', for the experiments. These cells are grown in flasks, Rogo says, and adhere so vigorously to the bottom that they cannot even be dislodged by powerful shaking:

The cells will only detach when they die, whereupon they float freely in the solution that fills the greater part of the container. Dr Kmetz wanted to see if Kraft could increase the number of dead cells in the solution merely by focusing his healing powers on the culture. The number of dead cells floating in the solution can be determined instrumentally by a haemacyclometer, so objective results could be made quickly by running counts before and after Kraft focused on the cultures.

A total of six experiments were conducted, in which Kmetz took Kraft and one of his lab assistants into a special room where the cultures were kept. Three flasks were used for each test. Kraft was given one flask to hold and told to focus on it. The lab assistant, who claimed no psychic abilities, was given another flask and told to treat it by copying whatever Kraft did with his. The third flask was left untouched as a control. The free-floating dead cancer cells in each flask were counted before and after each trial and those in the flask held by Kraft showed a 300 per cent increase of dead cells over the pre-trial measure. No significant changes were found in either the control flask or that held by the lab assistant. The young healer succeeded in obtaining the same level of success twice more during the six experiments but had to withdraw from further testing when he fell ill. But more trials and confirmations were hardly necessary and Kmetz reported the results in the 3 October 1977 issue of the *Hospital Tribune*.

'Nor was this the end of Dr Kmetz's research into the wonders of psychic healing,' Rogo writes in his 1987 book. 'He was later to replicate this experiment using cervical cancer cells. The healer for this later, and as yet unpublished, experiment was Matthew Manning, the well-known British psychic and healer. He, too, was able to kill the cells without any direct contact with them.'

Manning himself tells us about the Kmetz research, in his book *No Faith Required*. The experimenter adopted the same protocol of using a non-psychic healer to duplicate everything that Manning did, but this series included tests in which the healer held the flask, others where he was not allowed to touch it, and even an experiment in which three flasks were taped together and he was told to influence the contents of just one of them. An additional element was introduced into the tests by putting Manning into a shielded room at times, and also shielding the flasks.

According to Manning:

The results were the most dramatic that I had achieved in any experiments in Texas or at the University of

California. It was observed that in all but two of the
trials there was a marked increase in the number of
detached, and therefore dead, cancer cells in the flasks
on which I had been concentrating, yet by comparison
there were no changes in any of the flasks treated by the
volunteer for control purposes. The number of dead
cells had been increased in those successful trials by
between 200 per cent and 1200 per cent . . . One of the
interesting features of this experiment was that I was
still able to exert a very significant influence over the
cells even if I was contained within a shielded room.
This suggests that whatever was causing the healing
was not electricity, magnetisim or electromagnetism as
none of these forces could have penetrated outside the
shielded room. The energy was also evidently highly
directional because in the eighth trial, when I was to
influence just one of the three flasks taped together in a
different room, that was exactly what happened. Only
the one flask on which I had been focusing my energies
showed any increase in the number of dead cells.

A fascinating aspect of these experiments is that the healers
apparently achieved very different effects. Asked to make
blood cells survive longer, they did so. Asked to kill cancer
cells, they did so. Does this mean that the human mind can
curse as well as cure? Or does the healing power have the
intelligence to identify those organisms or cells which need a
boost and those which must be eradicated?

Now Manning heals people

It is said that in 1977 Manning had a powerful yet inexplicable
experience high in the Himalayan mountains, after which
he vowed only to become involved in research which might
benefit others. It also seems that, having seen how his powers
could affect biological systems in laboratories, Manning
decided to use them to good effect on people. I witnessed this
at one of his Mind, Body, Spirit healing workshops in 1997,

when he invited a handful of sufferers, whose conditions lent themselves to demonstrable improvement, to join him on the platform, one at a time, and receive treatment. Manning's methods are similar to those of Harry Edwards, though his results take much longer to achieve and there are long periods of silence as he focuses on the patient. Some members of the workshop audience were fidgety during these quiet periods, but most seemed mesmerised by his bold turquoise, blue and black zig-zag patterned designer jacket, as well as being intrigued by what was or was not happening to the patient. There is no denying that he achieves results.

One of those who received healing was Kay Sinclair, a London nursery manager, who had been involved in a car crash in January 1996. She'd driven into the back of another vehicle at 30 mph and, though X-rays showed no damage, she was suffering a lot of pain, had difficulty raising her left arm and experienced a pins-and-needles sensation when she did so. She was also unable to bend forward more than halfway. Manning's healing power got to work on her, and when he had finished, Miss Sinclair happily demonstrated a new-found freedom of movement and the disappearance of pain.

Nearly a year later I phoned her to check whether the improvement had been maintained or was just a five-minute wonder. 'I experienced a dramatic feeling that day,' she recalled. 'And there was no doubt that I was cured. Within a month I took a holiday to Jamaica, which I had been dreading because I didn't know how I was going to manage carrying my suitcase and travelling that distance. But I had no trouble at all. Now, I occasionally get tension in my neck and some discomfort, but nothing like the pain I suffered before seeing Matthew Manning.'

Rabbi who could heal mice

At about the same time as Matthew Manning and Dean Kraft were being tested in San Antonio, Texas, another team of researchers, headed by Roger MacDonald at the Washington

Research Center in San Francisco, was embarking on one of the most thorough and critical studies of spiritual healing ever undertaken. They began by surveying the published results of all earlier healing projects, then set about trying to replicate them in order to isolate a stable effect. They knew from their review of past studies that gifted healers were reported to have affected electrical and magnetic fields, the crystallisation process of copper salt, the growth rate of plants and the blood pressure of hypertensive animals, as well as inhibiting the growth of bacteria. They called in some of the best American healers, including the Rev. John Scudder of Homewood, Illinois; Dean Kraft, from New York; and Olga Worrall of Baltimore. Yet most of the experiments failed. Only the plant growth tests, using beakers of water imbued with healing energy, yielded positive results, and it was Olga Worrall's plants that flourished the most – growing some 25 per cent taller than the control plants.

Healing, it seems, does not always work well in the laboratory. Perhaps there are too many variables to guarantee consistent results. Yet there are enough reports of significant effects, from scientists and doctors whose expertise is beyond question, to say with confidence that the healing effect *has* been demonstrated in scientific tests.

In the mid-1970s, for example, Gary Null, then head of the Nutrition Institute of America and science director for the New York-based Institute of Applied Biology, conducted some remarkable tests over several years in collaboration with a number of colleagues. After travelling the world interviewing healers and documenting case studies, they were left wondering whether the successes they were told about were really due to an invisible healing force or the result of patients curing themselves with their own will-power.

To test this theory, they decided to use animals instead of humans in their experiments. These were designed to test whether healers could prolong the lives of mice which had been inoculated with cancer cells. They also assessed the healing potential of fifty healers and found only one who they felt was successful enough to invite back for further testing.

Unusually, he was a rabbi and cantor from New York, Rabbi Abraham Weisman, who had discovered his own healing powers after seeking help from another healer for a comparatively minor complaint.

For a three-week period in July 1977, Weisman was asked to give healing to ten one-year-old female white mice which had been injected with Ehrlich adenocarcinoma ascites fluid, which causes fatal tumours. He was not allowed to touch them, but held his hand over their cage. Ten other mice, similarly injected, did not receive healing. They died from cancer within an average of 8.9 days, whereas the treated mice lived an average of 12.8 days or 43.8 per cent longer. Null and his associates were amazed that some mice actually lived up to 18 or 19 days.

Mice had featured in the experiments of one of the earliest spiritual healing researchers, Dr Bernard Grad of McGill University, Canada. In the early 1960s he removed small patches of skin from the backs of 48 mice under anaesthetic, then divided them into three groups. One group was left untouched. The second was treated by healer Oskar Estebany who ran his hand over their backs, and the third group were exposed to heat at the same temperature as Estebany's hands. The wounds of the mice treated by Estebany healed much faster than either of the other two groups. Dr Grad repeated this experiment at the University of Manitoba using far more mice – a total of 300 – with exactly the same results.

He then went on to explore healing further by conducting tests with barley seeds which were placed in a saline solution, discovering that those immersed in liquid 'treated' by healers grew at a faster rate than those in untreated liquid. Dr Grad then extended the experiment to see what effect a person's state of mind might have on plant growth. Three individuals were selected for this test: a 26-year-old depressed woman, a psychotic man of the same age, and a gardener noted for his green fingers. They each produced different results. He came to the conclusion that an energy was at work which could make a difference to humans, animals and plants and that the phenomenon of 'green fingers' may be another expression of healing.

Another researcher doing similar work was the Rev. Franklin Loehr, a congregational minister with a master's degree in chemistry, who used 150 volunteers trained in disciplined prayer to concentrate on 27,000 seeds. More than 100,000 measurements were taken, and they revealed a striking difference between the growth of plants receiving prayer and those which did not.

Enzymes and seeds respond to healing

Meanwhile, Sister Justa Smith, an enzymologist and chairman of the chemistry department at Rosary Hill College in Buffalo, New York, was studying the effect of healing on enzymes. Having demonstrated that enzyme activity is increased by magnetic fields and damaged by ultraviolet light, she asked healer Oskar Estebany to take part in daily trials to compare what effect his healing hands had on enzymes. Each day four vials were used. Estebany would hold one for seventy-five minutes. A second was untouched but kept at the same temperature as his hands. The enzymes in the third were damaged by ultraviolet light and then treated by the healer for seventy-five minutes. And the fourth vial was subjected to a high magnetic field. Dr Smith reported a significant increase in the enzyme activity of the treated vials. The activity of the enzymes in the vial first treated by the healer, for example, was found to be the same as the vial subjected to a magnetic field of 13,000 gauss. Even more remarkable, perhaps, was the effect on the enzymes damaged by ultraviolet light and then treated by Estebany. They were found to be 'healed' and brought back to normal activity.

Testing the power of therapeutic touch

In 1990, Daniel P. Wirth reported, in the journal *Subtle Energies*, on experiments in which human subjects were used to test the power of non-contact therapeutic touch. Using a skin punch biopsy instrument, full-thickness wounds were cut on the lateral deltoid region of healthy subjects. Their wounds were then dressed and they were divided randomly into treatment or control groups but not told which, nor the purpose of the experiment. Each day they received five minutes' exposure to a hidden therapeutic touch practitioner or a sham exposure. Their wounds were measured on the first, eighth and sixteenth days and the results were highly significant. The wounds of all the twenty-three subjects who had (without knowing it) received actual therapeutic treatment were completely healed, whereas not a single one of the twenty-one control subjects (exposed to sham treatment) was totally healed.

A year later, the same journal, which is at the cutting edge of healing research, published a paper by William G. Braud, Ph.D, and Marilyn J. Schlitz, MA, which described a thirteen-year-long, and still continuing, series of laboratory experiments demonstrating that certain persons are able 'to exert direct mental influences upon a variety of biological systems that are situated at a distance from the influencer and shielded from all conventional informational and energetic influences.' (Braud had carried out similar experiments with Manning in 1977.)

According to Braud and Schlitz:

> The target system is monitored while, in a distant room, a person attempts to influence the system's activity in a pre-specified manner using mental processes of intentionality, focused attention, and imagery of desired outcomes. The experimental design rules out subtle cues, recording errors, expectancy and suggestion ('placebo') effects, artifactual reactions to external stimuli, confounding internal rhythms, and coincidental or chance correspondences.

So what, exactly, is the person influencing at a distance? Another person's electrodermal activity, blood pressure, and muscular activity; the spatial orientation of fish; the activity of small mammals; and the rate of haemolysis of human red blood cells, the researchers tell us.

The following year, London-based researcher Daniel J. Benor, MD, provided *Subtle Energies* readers with a review of a substantial body of studies which show 'that healing may bring about changes in water, enzymes, unicellular organisms, plants, animals and humans'. And in 1995 he added a report of two of his own experiments designed to see if a blindfolded subject could detect the presence of an experimenter's hand placed a few inches above one of theirs. Two-thirds of the time, he reported, they got it right, whereas chance predicted a 50–50 result.

But Emily Rosa, aged nine, had a different story to tell. She devised a simple test as an entry in her school's science fair in Loveland, Colorado. A cardboard box was built and she persuaded twenty-one therapeutic touch healers to put their hands into it and try to detect her energy field by identifying which of her hands was beneath theirs. They failed even to achieve a chance result, getting it right on average only 44 per cent of the time, compared with the over 50 per cent response required for it to be significant. Two years later, in 1998, Rosa's findings made international news after being published in the prestigious *Journal of the American Medical Association*. But Dolores Krieger, founder of therapeutic touch, dismissed the paper as 'poor in design and methodology' and other practitioners were quick to point out that the technique is used to restore energy imbalances in the sick and that there is no reason why a healer should know whether the part of the body he or she is treating is a left or a right hand.

So, despite all the laboratory experiments and learned papers, the scientific world and the public at large, it seems, continue to argue over the reality or otherwise of healing power.

That might change, in time, however, as a result of research being conducted in the UK by Toni Bunnell, who lectures in physiology at Hull University's Faculty of Health at Humberside, in north-east England. Dr Bunnell, who obtained her PhD in zoology in 1982, is both a scientist and a healer. She knows from personal experience that healing works, but her scientific curiosity has led her to conduct a major healing experiment and she is planning others.

'My interest in the subject began when I received healing after my father died,' she told me, speaking from the university. 'I felt better for it and decided to take a National Federation of Spiritual Healers' training course in Leeds so that I could offer healing to others. I now have a healing room set up in my home where I treat patients. But I also wanted to know how it worked and so I started my own studies in 1996.'

Dr Bunnell was particularly interested in the research carried out by Sister Justa Smith with enzymes (mentioned earlier) but critical of it because it was not an extensive study and she made a false assumption about the results. But Bunnell was keen to work with enzymes, too – in her case peptin – because they are known to be affected by magnetism. This opens up the possibility of comparing magnetic and healing influence on the enzyme being studied. Her results, confirming that the healing force did have a measurable effect, were published in the December 1996 issue of the *International Journal of Research in Complementary Medicine* and subsequent work has confirmed her findings. Now Dr Bunnell is extending her research activities and is planning to study the effect of healing on asthmatics and then on brainwaves.

Whether such research will silence the critics remains to be seen. What is beyond doubt is that, even if laying-on-of-hands was found to have a scientific basis, intense controversy would continue to surround those healers – called psychic surgeons – who claim to be able to cure people by opening up their bodies and carrying out operations with their bare hands.

6

PSYCHIC SURGERY

Seeing is believing. But in the case of psychic surgery there are many who doubt the evidence of their own eyes. Having seen it myself, I know exactly how they feel.

In the 1960s reports began reaching England of healers with the most extraordinary powers. Apparently they could perform surgery on their patients using everyday instruments, such as a kitchen knife, or even their bare hands. They removed tumours or other bloody masses from their patients, then closed the wounds instantly. Just as astonishing was the claim that those who were prepared to be 'operated' on in this way felt no pain, suffered no complications from the fact that the instruments used were not sterilised, and in many cases appeared to experience a complete cure.

I was then assistant editor of the world's only weekly spiritualist newspaper, *Psychic News*, and had a unique opportunity to discuss such claims with those who had witnessed these rather gruesome spectacles – which seem to be confined largely to Brazil and the Philippines. One of my first informants was American astronaut Edgar Mitchell, lunar module pilot during the Apollo 14 mission and the sixth man to walk on the moon. When we met in London we naturally discussed his moon mission but he was just as eager to tell me about his psychic research studies, which had included an extra-sensory perception experiment he had conducted from the lunar surface. After retiring from the American Navy, Mitchell had founded and become president of the Institute of Noetic Sciences, which had been set up to search for solutions to human problems and the release of human potential.

Mitchell was particularly enthusiastic about a young Israeli man, Uri Geller, whom he had seen bending metal, apparently by the power of his thought. Geller was then largely unknown, except by a small group of researchers who had been studying his claims and by nightclub audiences in his native country who had seen him perform. Little did I realise that very soon *everybody* would know his name. But Mitchell also told me about the healing research of Dr Henry Puharich and recommended that I interviewed him on his next trip to the UK.

Doctor has psychic operation

What I heard from Puharich at that meeting was mind-blowing. Here was a medical man who was willing to testify not only that psychic surgery was a real phenomenon but also that he had been operated on by a psychic surgeon. He rolled up the sleeve of his right arm and pointed to an area near his elbow. For seven years at that point, he explained, there had been a lipoma – a benign, fatty tumour that rolls around freely under the skin when it is examined. His doctor had checked it regularly and had recommended that Puharich should not have it surgically removed, since it was not causing him any problems. The doctor's concern was that it was directly over the ulnar nerve, which controls the movement of the hand, and also close to the brachial artery. There was a small risk that either of these might be damaged in the otherwise simple, twenty-minute operation to remove the lipoma, causing complications which might affect his finger control.

So where was the lipoma now? It had been removed, Puharich explained, by one of the most famous people in Brazil: a largely uneducated peasant, José Arigó, who was credited with having performed thousands of psychic operations. Puharich and an American medical team had first seen

Arigó at work in his 'clinic' at Congonhas do Campo, Minas Gerais, in August 1963 and their studies continued intermittently until 1968.

It was here that Arigó had been born in 1918. His real name was José Pedro de Freitas, but he was soon given the nickname Arigó (which means in Portuguese 'a simple individual, a rustic, a crude but easy-going yokel, a good fellow') because it summed him up perfectly. And it was here that thousands came every week, from all over Brazil, in the hope that the psychic surgeon (who made no charge for his services) could help them, when all other treatments had failed.

Puharich and his team filmed what happened. They were astonished to see Arigó introduce an unsterilised knife between the eye and eyelid of a patient, who was standing casually against a wall, then thrust it around almost violently. Yet the patient showed no sign of discomfort and reported improvement in his condition after the 'operation'. This was a procedure they witnessed many times. Puharich confessed that watching Arigó doing surgery without anaesthesia or antisepsis and seeing every principle of surgery violated with impunity 'was truly a mind-shattering experience'. Every patient was helped, and none had post-operative complications. It was so unlike anything he had experienced before, he added, that 'I found myself unable to accept the data of my own senses'.

Despite seeing it with his own eyes and having an extensive film record of psychic surgery being performed by Arigó, Puharich knew there was only one way to clinch the matter. He had to have psychic surgery himself, and the lipoma on his arm gave him the opportunity. Puharich gives a full account of what happened next in his contribution to Edgar Mitchell's massive study *Psychic Exploration: a challenge for science*:

The operation scene was a room in which some 90 people crowded around Arigó to see him operate. Arigó with a flourish requested that someone furnish him with a pocket knife, and someone in the audience

produced one. Arigó took hold of my right wrist with
his left hand and wielded the borrowed pocket knife
with his right hand. I was told not to watch the
operation on my right arm, so I turned my head toward
my cameraman and directed the motion-picture work.
The next thing I knew was that Arigó had placed a
tumour and the knife in my hand. In spite of being
perfectly conscious, I had not felt any pain. In fact, I
had no sensation at all at the surgical site. I was sure
that I had not been hypnotised. Yet there was the
incision in my arm. Subsequent analysis of the film
showed that the entire operation lasted five seconds.
Arigó had made two strokes with the knife on the skin.
The skin had split wide open, and the tumour was
clearly visible. Arigó then squeezed the tumour as one
might squeeze a boil, and the tumour popped out.

Despite the lack of the precautions usually considered necessary when performing surgery, Puharich suffered neither
infection nor blood poisoning and the wound healed in three
days – twice as fast as one would have expected.

This was a comparatively simple operation for Arigó who
is said to have performed heart surgery, removed cancerous
growths and treated practically every condition imaginable,
either by carrying out psychic operations or by issuing prescriptions, produced at lightning speed. (These always seemed
to work, despite the doubts of the doctors and pharmacists
who read them.) Many surgeons brought their patients to him
and even underwent surgery themselves. Their testimonies
make an impressive contribution to the vast body of evidence
which suggests that, however much our minds might shy
away from accepting such 'impossible' events, they happened
exactly as the well-trained observers reported.

Brazil's president adds his testimony

Among the medical men willing to testify was a qualified
physician, Juscelino Kubitschek, who had specialised in

surgery in Paris and the Middle East, and had served as a medical officer in various government agencies in Brazil for many years afterwards. But then his interest in politics took over and by the time he met Arigó for the first time he was the newly elected President of Brazil, the man who was to create the astonishing new capital, Brasilía, at the very centre of this huge country.

Visiting Congonhas do Campo with his wife one day, he decided to visit the famous psychic surgeon. 'Being a physician and surgeon myself,' he later testified, 'I found him so extraordinary that I cannot find words to express it. The people had faith in him. No one could fail to do so. He was a *god*.' Out of that meeting, a friendship developed.

Some time later, one of Kubitschek's daughters had to be flown to the United States for surgery to correct a critical and massive deformation of the spine. This delicate operation required her to remain completely immobilised for many months and that, in turn, caused two enormous kidney stones to form after she returned to Rio de Janeiro.

Kubitschek's wife was very, very nervous, because this complication could lead to a serious and perhaps lethal condition, he later explained:

She said to me: 'Could we ask Arigó to come down to Rio and see what he could do for our daughter?' I agreed. I reached Arigó by phone. I told him our daughter was critically ill, but did not tell him what the problem was. Congonhas do Campo is a six-hour drive, but he was here in Rio the next afternoon. He came into our home, and before I had a chance to tell him anything about my daughter's condition, he handed me a prescription written on a plain piece of paper. As a doctor I recognised that it was a specific for eliminating kidney stones. But how could Arigó know her condition? Since I had not been practising in recent times, I checked it with my own doctor. He indicated that he didn't feel it would do much good, but felt there would be no harm in trying it. Arigó's prescriptions were said to have an effect entirely beyond the bounds of the prescription itself. I gave her the medicine and she became completely cured.

To express their appreciation, the Kubitscheks presented Arigó with a solid gold wristwatch but he rejected it. He could not accept either money or gifts for his healing, he explained. Indeed, although he could have earned a fortune from the many wealthy and famous people who sought his aid, he insisted on doing a 'day job' in the local pension and welfare office in order to earn enough to feed himself and his family.

Imprisoned for healing the sick

But Arigó also had his enemies. There were medical men who were jealous of the crowds who sought his help and who felt this uneducated man was undermining their authority. And there were priests who felt similarly threatened by his popularity and who argued that Arigó was practising witchcraft. In fact, there was no doubt that, by performing his operations, Arigó was breaking the law and the time came when he had to face the consequences. On 26 March 1957 he was sentenced to fifteen months' imprisonment, but his lawyers prevented the sentence being carried out immediately.

In May the following year, Kubitschek issued a presidential pardon, which released Arigó from the threat of imprisonment. But Kubitschek had been swept from power by October 1964, when another court decided it had enough evidence to charge Arigó with practising witchcraft. Arigó stood trial the following month and was sentenced to sixteen months in jail. But such was the outcry from his thousands of supporters, many of them very influential, that he served only seven months before being released while a judicial review of the case was conducted. Judge Immesi was the man charged with this responsibility and, as part of his investigation, he decided to watch Arigó performing his operations. He wrote in a report:

> I saw him pick up what looked like a pair of nail
> scissors. He wiped them on his sport shirt, and used no
> disinfectant of any kind. Then I saw him cut straight
> into the cornea of the patient's eye. She did not blench,
> although she was fully conscious. The cataract was out
> in a matter of seconds. The district attorney and I were
> speechless, amazed. Then Arigó said some kind of
> prayer, as he held a piece of cotton in his hand. A few
> drops of a liquid suddenly appeared on the cotton, and
> he wiped the woman's eye with it. We saw this at close
> range. She was cured.

Though there was no doubt in the judge's mind that Arigó possessed extraordinary powers, the fact remained that, in performing these operations, he was breaking the law. He had to return him to jail ... but this time for just two months. In fact, though he was upset to be separated from his family, the term of imprisonment was not as onerous for Arigó as some might imagine. The prison officers even allowed him out, at times, to visit the sick and eventually the prison started to resemble a hospital, with a queue of sufferers forming outside and being allowed in to consult the psychic surgeon one at a time.

Stories abound about Arigó. Most of them, I suspect, are true, including his healing of the infant son of Brazil's top singer and entertainer, Roberto Carlos. This child was born with a serious fulminant glaucoma condition, an intense form of inflammation causing total loss of sight and light perception. Roberto Carlos and his wife rushed the child to European specialists who declared him incurable. But, on their return to Brazil, Carlos chartered a plane and flew to Lafaiete, then took the boy by car to see the psychic surgeon. The details of Arigó's surgery have never been revealed but within days the infant's sight was restored.

Surgeon of the rusty knife

John Fuller did a superb job of collecting much of the

evidence, including a stack of medical testimonies, and weaving it into his excellent biography of the healer, *Arigó: Surgeon of the Rusty Knife*.

As well as curing thousands of sick people, Arigó opened the minds of many more to the possibility of a spiritual dimension to life. It also looked, at one time, as if his work might be scientifically verified beyond any shadow of doubt. There was talk of setting up a full-scale medical investigation and establishing a hospital in which he could work. These hopes were never realised.

Early in 1971 President Kubitschek, now back in Brazil and enjoying renewed popularity, sensed something was wrong while visiting his friend. 'I am sure I will die violently very soon,' Arigó told him. 'So I say goodbye to you with sadness. This is the last time we will meet.' And to another good friend, Gabriel Khater, he said, 'I am afraid, Gabriel, that my mission on earth is finished.'

A few days later, on 11 January 1971, Arigó's extraordinary life came to a sudden end in a car crash. It seems that he died of a heart attack at the wheel and then his car smashed into another, killing two of its occupants.

Having talked to Puharich about his experiences and interviewed others, I was satisfied that Arigó had demonstrated a real psychic phenomenon which achieved astonishing healing results. That opinion was reinforced when I viewed a film of Arigó at work and saw with my own eyes some of the psychic surgery being performed. It was not for the squeamish and I confess I had to avert my gaze at times. Arigó apparently had the same problem. He did these operations while in a trance, and it is said that when he first saw a film of himself performing surgery he fainted.

Lourival de Freitas takes London by storm

Despite the strength of the evidence concerning Arigó, it was still second-hand. As a young reporter specialising in the paranormal, it remained my ambition to witness psychic surgery for myself. Brazil and the Philippines – where other psychic surgeons were reported to be working – were beyond my reach. But my wish was soon granted with the arrival in London, in July 1966, of Lourival de Freitas. I had read just one report of an operation this Brazilian had performed and, as far as I knew, his techniques were similar to those of Arigó. Accompanied by an interpreter, he called unannounced at the offices of *Psychic News* and my colleague Anne Dooley interviewed him. To her surprise, and ours, Lourival de Freitas said he was prepared to demonstrate his healing powers in London to anyone we cared to invite to a special meeting. It was an opportunity we could not afford to miss.

At very short notice a venue was organised and a selected audience of leading healers and others interested in the claims of psychic surgeons gathered for the big occasion. Maurice Barbanell, the newspaper's editor, persuaded a number of brave individuals to be operated on by the psychic surgeon and I dashed out to buy everything Lourival de Freitas said he would need for the surgery. I came back with a wooden-handled kitchen knife from a local branch of Woolworth's, a bag of cotton wool, scissors and a bottle of whisky. We wondered whether the whisky was to be used as some form of antiseptic, but as soon as the healer arrived for the demonstration, dressed in heavy and colourful robes, we realised that he planned to drink it . . . straight from the bottle. Later, we were told that in his normal state Lourival de Freltas did not touch alcohol, but when entranced by the spirits who performed the surgery it was not unusual for him to down a whole bottle of whisky.

I had taken an 8 mm cine camera as well as my reporter's notebook, and I began to film the expressions of awe, astonishment and excitement on the faces of the witnesses, sitting patiently around the beautiful, wood-panelled lecture hall of the Spiritualist Association of Great Britain's headquarters in Belgrave Square. Impatience was another emotion which they soon exhibited, as Lourival de Freitas interrupted his examinations of patients with loud singing, to his own guitar accompaniment, and further swigs of whisky. After three hours nothing much had happened, although we were assured that the 'entertainment' was necessary to build up the energy so that psychic surgery could be performed.

One of his patients was a woman with cataracts. He suddenly pushed the kitchen knife under her eyelid, then covered both her eyes with cotton wool and left her stretched out on a table while he turned his attention to a second volunteer. This was a man suffering from stomach cancer who had been given only a few weeks to live. His wife and doctor had kept this news from him and the Brazilian psychic surgeon was his wife's last hope. Lourival de Freitas asked the man to open his mouth, then jabbed a pair of scissors into the back of his throat, causing him to gag. He then put cotton wool into the man's mouth to soak up some of the blood and when he removed it, on the end of the scissors, he revealed what appeared to be small lumps of gristle, or tumours. The man spat more bloody liquid into a bowl and the healer then went back to his cataract patient. He took a glass of water and, using the kitchen knife, appeared to remove a cataract from her eye and drop it into the liquid so that we could see it.

Our photographer had been told not to take any flash photographs until Lourival de Freitas gave permission but, with events apparently picking up, she decided he might have forgotten and so she took a picture. The healer – or the spirit controlling him – immediately threw a tantrum . . . and the knife. It buried itself in the wood panelling just a foot or so above the heads of his illustrious audience. It was all too much for the Spiritualist Association councillors who had given permission for the demonstration. Not only were they worried about the well-being of the patients but they now had concerns for the very fabric of their building. They called a halt. The interpreter had to explain the decision to the entranced healer, who seemed prepared to carry on well into the small hours. And we all staggered home, shell-shocked and confused after an extraordinary episode.

The sad truth is that the man with cancer died soon afterwards, as the doctor had expected, and when the woman returned to her eye specialist he found the cataract still intact but remarked on the presence of scratches on her eye.

Famous healer Harry Edwards, one of the witnesses to this incredible demonstration, had no hesitation in dismissing it as fraud. And Gordon Turner, another well-known healer, said he hoped we had 'seen the last' of this type of healing in the UK.

Anne Dooley, however, was not convinced that Lourival de Freitas was a fraud. She later watched him perform other operations in Britain and even travelled to Brazil to see him at work. There he carried out psychic surgery on her lungs, she reported, and her book *Every Wall a Door* not only includes a detailed account of this experience but also contains a rather grisly photograph of a long, sewn-up wound down her back, with the healer pulling her skin away from the body by the stitches. Nevertheless, Anne Dooley maintained that the surgery brought about a vast improvement in the lung condition which had plagued her for many years.

Fakes in the Philippines

The cry of fraud has also been heard with increasing frequency from visitors to the Philippines who have sought the help of its famous psychic surgeons. The very first to demonstrate such surgery was Eleuterio Terte, a leading figure in the Philippines Christian Spiritualist movement. Since then, dozens have appeared, each with a special reputation for performing miracles, usually without the need of any instrument.

The problem is that most people are easily taken in by simple sleight-of-hand tricks and refuse to believe that the individuals they are consulting, who talk at length about God and the Bible, might be charlatans. Yet there is no doubting the evidence that fraud is prevalent. Tests done on blood and other substances apparently removed from patients are frequently shown to be of animal origin. Photographs of human eyes being lifted out of their sockets by psychic surgeons are also clearly not human at all. To add to the confusion, some healers claim to remove worms, plastic, nails, coins and a bewildering range of other 'foreign objects' from their patients' bodies. Despite all that, there are many testimonies – including some from doctors – to the benefits received from such treatment and I have spoken to several people, including healers, who have been to the Philippines and are satisfied that what they saw is authentic.

To an untrained eye – even that of a doctor – the psychic surgeon seems to knead his patient's skin until an opening occurs, blood begins to trickle out, and then suddenly his hand plunges deep inside the cavity before pulling out blood clots, tumours or other bloody items. What a conjuror sees is something different. The healer appears to have nothing in his hands, but has a small nylon bag containing animal blood hidden in the folds of his palm. As he kneads the patient's body – usually in one of the fleshiest areas, such as the stomach – he squeezes the bag and blood flows. He then plunges his hand into the flesh, bending his fingers as he does so to give the illusion that his hand is deep inside a bloody cavity. From this he produces substances which he has either introduced with his other hand, or which have been passed to him hidden inside cotton wool by one of his assistants. It looks real. It looks gruesome. But it's a sham.

Even the Filipino healers themselves agree on that. At least, most accuse the others of being fakes while insisting on their own genuineness. One outspoken healer is Arsenia dela Cruz, daughter of the famous Eleuterio Terte, who since her father's death prefers not to carry out operations. Instead she uses magnetic healing or the laying-on-of-hands which she insists is even more effective. Talking to Gert Chesi, author of the excellent and lavishly illustrated *Faith Healers in the Philippines*, she said 90 per cent of all patients are the victims of an optical illusion and she even demonstrated how the sleight of hand is performed, with the evidence disappearing, along with the cotton wool, into a bucket. She believes there is hardly a healer in Baguio City, where most of them are based, who does not resort to tricks of some kind.

Gert Chesi was enormously impressed when he first saw Filipino psychic surgeons at work, but soon changed his mind on a return visit. He writes:

My second trip brought me back down to earth. I
realised that my naive enthusiasm had blinded me and I
would have to deal with the negative aspects of faith
healing – the commercialism and the trickery – as well. I
am, however, fully aware of the fact that it is no easy
matter to determine precisely where authenticity ends
and fakery begins. The central experience is without
doubt the 'bloody operation'. At this point in my
research I am almost fully convinced that these
operations are rarely genuine, if ever. They involve
sleight of hand in some form or other, even if it is not
always visible to the spectator. That does not mean that
simulated operations are a complete hoax. I am sure
that they can trigger off the healing process through
auto-suggestion . . . Most Philippine doctors and healers
I have talked to were of the opinion that sleight of hand,
whenever it results in success, can and must be regarded
as a perfectly legitimate method of treatment.

In other words, it's the placebo effect again. But that is no
reason to turn a blind eye to blatant fraud. Which is why,
some years ago, the American Federal Trade Commission
cracked down on travel agencies that booked tours to the
Philippines, prohibiting them from using the words 'psychic
surgery' in their advertising.

In his masterly book, *The Roots of Consciousness*, psychologist Dr Jeffrey Mishlove reveals that when he and his
wife Janelle watched over 20 psychic operations carried out
in Manila by Alex Orbito, president of the Philippine Healers
Association and one of the most prominent and respected
healers, Janelle concluded that sleight of hand could explain
everything they saw. Mishlove agreed that it was possible,
but regarded the hypothesis as unproved. 'Other observers,
such as Canadian psychologist Lee Pulo, have observed and
filmed hundreds of sessions with Orbito and are convinced
that they are genuine,' Mishlove writes.

A psychic surgeon who has clearly made a bigger impact
on him is Dona Pachita, a Mexican healer who treats her

patients while entranced by an Aztec prince, Cuahutemoc. Among those who have watched her at work and testified to the results is psychologist Alberto Villoldo who acted as her assistant during surgery on a Texas woman. Using an unsterilised hunting knife, Pachita apparently opened the woman's abdomen and removed a cancerous tumour from her urinary bladder, replacing it with a new human bladder which was purportedly obtained from a local medical school.

One of the witnesses to this operation, in which Villoldo removed tissues from the abdomen under the healer's instructions, was an American medical doctor, Gabriel Cousens, who declared: 'There was no question in my mind that she was opening the skin: there was no question that I was smelling blood. I could see the opening in the abdomen . . . and I could see Pachita's hands going into the bladder area, into the abdominal cavity . . . I had no doubts that I had seen authentic "psychic surgery".'

Joao de Deus – the new Arigó?

When Henry Puharich received a phone call in his New York office telling him that Brazilian psychic surgeon José Arigó had been killed in a car crash it had a profound effect on him. He wrote about it in a postscript to John Fuller's *Arigó: Surgeon of the Rusty Knife*:

> I sat back in my chair. It was not possible for Arigó, the greatest healer in the world, to be dead! He was too young, too vital. Besides, he was the hope of thousands, perhaps millions of people who looked to him as the witness to higher powers. There must be a mistake, I thought. I had to check this out myself. I called friends in Brazil, who confirmed the dread news that Arigó had been killed in an auto accident. I was personally despondent. The loss of Arigó to me was as if the sun had gone out; the planet earth and humanity had lost their great luminary. I had suddenly become impoverished. The shock was so deep to me that I decided to go on a fourteen-day fast and re-examine all

my life, to weigh the meaning of Arigó, in life and in death.

Near the end of my fast, I came to some strong personal conclusions. The first was that I had failed both Arigó and humanity by not completing my studies of Arigó's healing work. I now realised that I should have dropped my other work in 1963 and concentrated all my efforts on him. I was sure there would never be another Arigó in my lifetime. But if there was, I would not fail the next time . . .

Would there be another Arigó? I wondered about that also as I began to write this book and I concluded that it was highly unlikely. The activities of fraudulent Filipino psychic surgeons have done so much harm that I felt no one in his or her right mind would try to develop such powers, assuming they exist. But then I heard about Joao Teixeria da Faria, better known throughout Brazil as Joao de Deus ('John of God').

Joao de Deus, it seems, *is* the new Arigó. A simple man who has dedicated his life to healing the sick, he performs operations every bit as astonishing as those of his fellow countryman, who died when he was twenty-nine. He also writes rapid prescriptions and gives mass 'invisible' healings to those who prefer to be made whole without having their troubles, and their insides, exposed to the outside world. And, like Arigó, he refuses payment.

According to Robert Pellegrino-Estrich, who is one of his grateful patients and has written a book about Joao de Deus, called *The Miracle Man*, he treats up to 3000 people a day and carries out more operations in twenty-four hours than a small hospital achieves in a month. Unlike Arigó, however, he uses groups of mediums to give him extra psychic energy in his work.

Actress Janet Leigh is one of the many celebrities who are said to have flown to his clinic in Central Brazil. And Shirley MacLaine was reported to have had a cancer removed from her abdomen by Joao de Deus in February 1991. Congressmen, statesmen, priests, nuns, rabbis and people from all walks of life are prepared to make the 36-hour journey from Saõ Paulo in order to be treated by him. Certificates of appreciation, orders of government and honorary degrees bestowed upon him by grateful dignitaries and institutions adorn his walls. They include a Medal of Honour from the President of Peru, in gratitude for healing his son.

Just like Arigó before him, Joao de Deus also faces the threat of legal action because he is breaking the law by treating the sick without medical qualifications. A writ for his arrest was issued in 1981 but his lawyers intervened in time to prevent him from going to jail. His supporters hint darkly at more sinister moves to stop him healing and claim there was an attempt on his life by four men the following year. More recently, in March 1995, three police officers arrived to arrest him but his legal representatives, Jaques Pereira and Sebastiao Soares, immediately filed for a *habeas corpus* to prevent the healer from being jailed. According to Robert Pellegrino-Estrich, 'The lawyers wisely approached Supreme Court Judge Antonio Feu Rosa who directed District Judge Joao Miguel Filho to issue the *habeas corpus*. Judge Feu Rosa had received an operation from Joao.' Other eminent figures in the legal establishment who are said to have sought Joao de Deus's healing help include Supreme Court Judge José de Oliveria Rosa and Minister of the Supreme Court, Justice Hilmar Haivao.

The healer is also said to be willing to perform psychic surgery under the close scrutiny of scientists and cameras. Tests by the Faculty of Medicine, Federal University de Juis de Forta, Minas Gerais, showed 'the surgery is genuine'. Alexander Moreira de Almeida, Tatiana Moreira de Almeida and Angela Maria Gollnere reported that they had 'observed a series of operations including scraping the eye cornea, the introduction of scissor-shaped tweezers tipped with cotton wool into the nasal cavity, the extraction of teeth, breast surgery and abdominal surgery and the surgical removal of a lipoma weighing 120 grams from a patient's back'. They also said 'pathological tests reveal that the removed substances are compatible with their origins and that they are human tissues . . .'

Doctor's brain tumour vanishes in three days

One of the most astonishing cases concerns a recently graduated doctor from Minas Gerais who developed a 2 inch (5 cm) wide brain tumour. Dr Klaun's family flew him to America where the best specialists in their respective fields – neurology, cancer and surgery – said he had a 50 per cent chance of surviving an operation to remove the tumour, and only a 20 per cent chance of leading a normal life if he did. The most likely scenario, if he lived through the operation, was that he would become a paraplegic.

Rather than face these risks, his family decided to seek the help of Joao de Deus. The young man's father, also a doctor, was aware of the healer's reputation because he worked at the Ministry of Health and received objections to the psychic surgeon's activities from medical associations as well as letters of praise from those who had been cured by him. Joao de Deus was optimistic that a total cure might be possible.

Dr Klaun arrived for his treatment, accompanied by his father and the two Brazilian doctors who had diagnosed the tumour. Rather than have actual surgery, he had requested an invisible operation which involved being placed in the centre's intensive operations room. He went into a coma and, for three days and nights, his body appeared not to function. On the fourth day, when he awoke, he was advised by Joao de Deus to have another X-ray. It showed that the tumour had completely gone.

Everyone who observed this astonishing change agreed to testify on video and so the patient, his father and the medical advisers recorded their stories, and showed the 'before' and 'after' X-rays. Today, over three years later, Dr Klaun is still alive and well, and there is no sign of the cancer returning.

Such stories are so unbelievable it is hardly surprising that many people refuse to accept them at face value . . . unless, of course, they are the ones who have been cured. It remains to be seen whether scientists will be able to study Joao de Deus in greater depth and with more success than was achieved with José Arigó. If so, it might finally be possible to transfer psychic surgery from the realm of apparent science fiction into that of science fact.

7

THE WORLD OF SPIRIT

If the discussion of psychic surgery in the previous chapter has pushed your credulity to the limit, you will find what I am about to tell you even harder to accept. Yet it is also based on eyewitness accounts of astonishing healings which took place not in Brazil or the Philippines but in a tiny healing sanctuary in the quiet English countryside. For at Pinewoods Healing Church, close to Newstead Abbey, Nottinghamshire, a medium regularly 'produced' the spirit of a dead surgeon, Dr Reynolds, who had died 150 years earlier, so that he could physically operate on the sick.

According to those who witnessed this remarkable phenomenon, Isa Northage was a 'materialisation' medium. This meant that when she went into a trance, in a darkened room – illuminated by only a red light – spirits of the dead would appear and talk to those present by cloaking their bodies in ectoplasm produced by the medium's body.

This is not the place to discuss the pros and cons of such claims in any depth, except to say that in the nineteenth century, when many more so-called physical mediums were conducting such seances, a number of eminent scientists, including Sir William Crookes, conducted experiments and satisfied themselves that the materialisation was genuine. Few individuals claim to have these powers today and so there is a great temptation to dismiss such accounts on the grounds that they come from gullible people who were duped. My response to that is to say that such stories are no more incredible than the reports of psychic surgery we have already encountered, and that we should be prepared to examine them, on the grounds that they may make an important contribution to our understanding of healing as a whole.

In fact, even though the events described below occurred some forty or fifty years ago, there are remarkable parallels between the techniques used in the English seance room and those used by modern-day psychic surgeons. For example, Dr Reynolds is said to have closed wounds after an operation simply by using his hands. He also made accurate diagnoses and gave prescriptions as part of his treatment. And witnesses speak of seeing his hands disappear into the patients' bodies. Those who wrote these accounts took every precaution to ensure that fraud was not occurring. The 'inner sanctuary' in which the seances took place was always securely locked before the start of proceedings, and the medium was often visible, seated in her chair, as the operations took place. The bearded Dr Reynolds' features were clearly visible and the witnesses commented on the differences in size, stature and voice between him, the other spirits who materialised, and the medium who was often visible in the dim light, seated in her chair, as the operations took place. Most remarkable of all was the way in which Dr Reynolds left the room. Witness after witness reported seeing him slowly dematerialise through the floor.

Laboratory confirms ulcer was removed

Ernest Thompson, editor of spiritualist publication *Two Worlds*, wrote this account after attending one of these seances in 1949:

> This is a story without parallel . . . on May 21st, I was privileged to witness, in Mrs Northage's operating theatre, two further amazing operations by Dr Reynolds and the following is a plain statement of facts

concerning the proceedings . . . Dr Reynolds'
materialised form appeared and was first discernible as
a black silhouette against the red glow from the lamp
on a trolley on which was laid forceps, two red electric
torches and two luminous plaques.

Picking up one of these torches, Dr Reynolds
switched it on and turned towards the operating table
on which lay a patient suffering from an acute
duodenal ulcer. He greeted everyone present, and as he
did so his face and ectoplasm draperies were visible to
us. He was of average height and shorter than Mrs
Northage . . . Dr Reynolds then prepared the patient,
placing a collection of cotton wool swabs on his
abdomen, and reassured him that he would feel no pain
whatsoever. No anaesthetic was used. The doctor then
said he would 'freeze' the portion of the body to be
operated upon and then pass his hand, which would
become dematerialised, into the side of the body and
remove the ulcer. His hands moved to the side of the
body and as he did so he asked the patient if he felt any
pain. The patient replied in the negative.

Then I heard a gurgling sound like the passage of
wind within the body. At this stage Dr Reynolds paused
and said that the ulcer was in a very bad condition and
would not come away in a whole piece and that he was
afraid of haemorrhage. This was apparently overcome
and the portions of ulcer brought through what Dr
Reynolds described as a temporary opening in the
abdomen, and placed on the swabs on the surface of
the body. He next cleared an opening amongst the
swabs and asked me to look down into it. It was
difficult, however, in the red light to see anything very
definite through this opening. He then proceeded to
remove some of the swabs with the forceps and placed
them on a tray which was held by one of his
assistants . . .'

At this point, Dr Reynolds dematerialised in order not to

drain the medium's powers too much. After a short break, the proceedings continued:

> Dr Reynolds returned once more to perform a second operation. This patient had recently had an accident in which the bone in his nose had splintered and had prevented him from breathing through his nose. This time the spirit doctor picked up a white electric torch and for a few seconds we saw him in the full glare of white light. He next picked up a red torch and proceeded to examine the patient, saying that he would dematerialise his hand, pass it through the back of his head, clean the bone and remove the splinters with a piece of lint. Dr Reynolds' hand was then seen to approach the back of the patient's head and apparently pass into it. When it was withdrawn his hand stretched out to place something in a second dish held by Mrs Stenson, one of his assistants. Dr Reynolds stated that he had collected three small pieces of bone . . .

Often after such spirit operations, the observers were under instructions to burn any matter removed from the bodies. On this occasion, however, the editor and a Mrs Difford, who acted as Dr Reynolds' assistant during the seances, took the two containers of used swabs into a room in Mrs Northage's house and used forceps to salvage the tissues and two pieces of bone, placing them into a bottle of surgical spirit, then throwing the bloodstained swabs into the fire.

'Before leaving,' Thompson continued, 'I interviewed both patients, the first stating that he felt quite well and had now no pain whatsoever, whereas he was in great pain before the operation. The second patient testified to the fact that he could now breathe freely through his nose whereas this had been impossible since his accident.'

Within a few days Thompson received the results of an analysis of the ulcer, which had been examined by a leading medical expert under the microscope in his laboratory. The scientist wrote: 'It is an acute duodenal ulcer, contains

Brunner's glands and shows from its condition that it was about to penetrate the intestine and would have proved fatal at a very early date.' He also expressed surprise at the freshness of the tissue which was very soft, and also at the fact that there was no trace of modern surgical methods having been used in the operation.

Former medical student's testimony

Among others who testified to the miraculous healing powers of the materialising surgeon was Group Captain G.S.M. Insall, an RAF pilot whose bravery had won him a Victoria Cross. His account, along with many others – all written in a very matter-of-fact way – appeared in the remarkable story of Isa Northage, *A Path Prepared*, by Allan MacDonald:

> . . . I was asked to attend and help with a couple of bloodless operations. I met the two patients in [Isa Northage's] sitting room. They were businessmen who had just driven from a Midland city about 50 miles away. They were both suffering from hernia, and one had complications. [. . .]
>
> We prepared the room, donned white overalls and masks, as was the rule with Dr Reynolds. This was not new to me as I had been a student in the most up-to-date French hospital before the First World War changed my career to flying. I had attended many an operation in those days, and some I would never put pen to paper to describe. But this bloodless one is a very different story. I will now proceed. The two patients came in. The first, the one with complications, was partially stripped and placed on the operating table. The other was given a chair nearby.
>
> There was a trolley and I checked over the instruments – tweezers, swabs, kidney basins and bowls; no cutting instruments at all except scissors to cut lint. There was also a small white pencil light. I checked the emergency door and saw that it was locked

and bolted on the inside, and draught excluded by a
mat placed on the threshold. I was just closing the inner
door leading into the church when somebody noticed
that the medium had not arrived. I opened it again, and
she came in. The light was turned low and somebody
opened in prayer. I could see the medium sitting in her
usual chair, a curtain hanging on either side.

Immediately the prayer was over a trumpet rose and
Dr Reynolds' familiar voice greeted us all. [. . .] The
trumpet went down and almost immediately the Doctor
appeared in materialised form on the opposite side of
the operating table . . . Then I saw him place his hands
on the patient's flesh, and they just went in deep, nearly
out of sight. He stretched out for the tweezers and
swabs and I collected eight soiled ones altogether.

Although Dr Reynolds said he was helped by a large team of
spirit doctors, some of whom were specialists in particular
diseases and materialised to perform surgery when patients
with those conditions attended, he also needed 'real' assistants in the 'operating theatre'. Sometimes these assistants,
called on to witness the surgery at close quarters, were the
patients' relatives.

'I could not believe my eyes'

When Edith Hands of Rubery, Birmingham, sought Dr
Reynolds' help for cancer, it was her husband John and
another man, Steve Fisher, who were called on to assist. They
watched as Dr Reynolds appeared, then swabbed the areas to
be operated on with a disinfectant. This is John Hands'
astonishing account of what happened next:

He then . . . passed his hand across the affected areas.
The patient's breasts were opened, and the abdomen
treated likewise. Dr Reynolds then took a bright green
pencil torch from the trolley and shone the light into
the cavities, showing three cancers lying deeply inside.

Doctor then explained that the cancer in the intestines had burst, and with swabs he removed the pieces, carefully placing each in a receptacle. He cleaned the site with swabs, each of which as it came from the wound was covered in blood and pus. There was a strange sound as each cancer was drawn from the breasts, and after this all wounds were carefully cleaned. The doctor not only removed the cancers but also the hairlike roots which, he said, would prevent the growths from re-forming. They were over most of her chest and abdomen, and while working in the region of her left armpit a hemorrhage started which caused the Doctor some concern, and he said he would have to fetch something from the spirit world to stop it. He disappeared through the floor, but in a few moments reappeared with a liquid with which he soaked a swab and pressed it under my wife's armpit, asking her to close her arm tightly against it . . .

On being satisfied that the wounds were clean, he gradually closed them up sideways, until only what appeared to be scratches were left. Then he placed his hands sideways on each wound and drew it across from end to end, and as his hand passed over the edges of the wounds they were sealed completely, not even a scratch remaining. Finding the haemorrhage had stopped, he sealed up that wound likewise.

During the operation, John Hands was passing swabs to the spirit doctor who worked so fast that 'he occasionally grabbed my fingers instead of the swab'. When the surgery was complete, Dr Reynolds said he wanted another surgeon, Dr West, to take a look at the patient.

'Stepping back about two feet from the table he sank through the floor, and within two minutes Dr West appeared in his place, the latter being of different height and build to Dr Reynolds. He said very little as he went over the patient's body with a torch, taking particular notice of the place where the bleeding had occurred.'

The operation, John Hands reported, took one hour and twenty minutes. 'When it was over we went outside, and Mr Fisher remarked that though he had witnessed everything that took place he just could not believe his eyes. That is just how I feel about it.'

As for Edith Hands, she said that 'gazing into Doctor's eyes as he operated', talking quite naturally, 'I had to think deeply to realise he was not of this world, but was indeed an angel.'

However difficult it may be for us to believe these accounts, they illustrate perfectly why healing is not, perhaps, more widely accepted by the scientific community. The spiritual or otherworldly dimension permeates the practice of healing and cannot be ignored. It is one thing to show that some mysterious healing force can apparently affect cells and seeds in a laboratory, and that laying-on-of-hands makes people better, but quite another to grapple with the claim that it is discarnate entities who are really responsible for such achievements.

Yet, time and again we encounter this belief and it needs to be confronted. The case of Isa Northage and Dr Reynolds is extreme because it really leaves us with no alternative explanation. Either the operations happened exactly as reported or they were the result of an elaborate and apparently motiveless fraud. And if Dr Reynolds was not a spirit surgeon and Mrs Northage was not a materialisation medium, then where did the fresh duodenal ulcer which seemed to have been removed without the aid of modern surgical instruments, come from?

Leading healers claim they work with spirit doctors

Let us cast our minds back to the remarkable psychic surgery of José Arigó. How did he, an uneducated peasant, manage to perform such miracles? His answer was simple. He was guided by a Dr Adolphus Fritz who would take over his body, in trance, to perform the operations and also write prescriptions. It was his voice which Arigó said he heard giving him the diagnoses. Dr Fritz identified himself as a German surgeon, killed during the 1914–18 war, and when Arigó received German patients Dr Fritz spoke to them in their language.

Other members of his spiritual medical team were said to be a French surgeon identified as Gilbert Pierre, responsible for ophthalmology, and a Japanese specialist named Takakashi, who removed tumours. The spirit of Fabiano de Cristo, a well-known friar famous in his lifetime for his charitable activities, was reputed to be responsible for producing a 'green light' to sterilise the environment, the instruments and the patients' wounds, together with the necessary anaesthesia so that no pain was felt. At one session, whilst dealing with a difficult case, 'Dr Fritz' was heard to ask for 'more green light, please.' Immediately, several people in the audience close to the medium lost consciousness, as though they had been anaesthetised.

And what about Joao de Deus, who emulates Arigó in so many ways? He, too, is helped by a band of spirit doctors as well as a few other influential souls. The principal spirit entity is Dom Inacio de Loyala, after whom the healing clinic is named. A Spanish nobleman, born in 1491 into a very rich family, his violent and aggressive nature served him well as an officer in the Spanish army. But, after seeing a vision of the Apostle Paul, which changed his outlook, and then a vision of the Virgin Mary, which totally transformed him, Dom Inacio became a beggar and dedicated his life to helping others. Another of Joao de Deus' spirit helpers is none other than King Solomon, who he says first manifested to him at the age of sixteen and continues to work closely with him.

Even Harry Edwards, England's most famous healer, believed that the spirits of Lord Lister, founder of antiseptic surgery, and Louis Pasteur, the French scientist, were members of the band of helpers in the next world who produced his healing results.

Similar beliefs are found in almost every culture. But the problem with all these claims – particularly those involving famous personalities – is that we have no way of knowing whether they are true or whether the healers concerned are just fantasising. Most healer–mediums whose bodies are apparently entranced by the spirit of a long-dead doctor can produce no evidence of the spirit's identity and in most cases there is not enough information even to begin investigating the claim.

Conjuring tricks or healing?

One of the most controversial British healers is Stephen Turoff who is described as a psychic surgeon but whose 'operations' are not as impressive as those performed in Brazil or the Philippines. Indeed, many of the techniques he uses, such as placing a glass containing a burning piece of material over a small incision on the patient's flesh, are regarded by skeptics as no more than well-known conjuring tricks. The flame burns the oxygen which causes a vacuum and that in turn sucks blood out of the cut. Turoff claims to be controlled during these operations by the spirit of Dr Joseph Abraham Kahn, a medical doctor who died in 1912. But neither he nor Dr Kahn has been able to provide proof that such a person ever existed.

Living with a psychic surgeon cannot be easy, but Kathy Turoff seems to take it in her stride. Turoff's biographer, Grant Solomon, who describes the healer as 'a 16-stone, six-and-a-half foot, middle-aged Jewish-Christian former carpenter from Brick Lane in London's East End' gives a wonderful account of his first visit to Turoff's clinic in a converted council house in Danbury, Essex. He had already met Turoff at a dinner in London and, accompanied by his mother, had decided to take his brother to the psychic surgeon for treatment:

We found ourselves in a crowded room with about 10 other people. Nearly everybody had either a wheelchair, crutches or bandages. Another 20 or so people who could stand unaided did so in a disorderly queue down the garden path. Not a business that makes for easy relations with the neighbours, I thought to myself. The four loudly clicking clocks, flower-patterned sofas and antique darkwood furniture added to the strange, almost spooky atmosphere.

Then the door was flung open and Stephen stormed past in a white coat. Well, I thought it was Stephen. But his wrinkled face looked a good 20 years older. He was round shouldered, as if slightly hunched, and he dragged his right leg along behind him as he rushed past us towards his wife, who was standing in the kitchen. He was physically smaller, enough to necessitate rolling his trousers up a couple of folds. I smiled to myself, wondering what my friends would make of it all, but came back to the room with a jolt when he spoke.

I have told you not to leave the bits in the sink,' he barked at Kathy in a distinctly German accent.

'Sorry, Dr Kahn,' said Kathy, apologetically, and proceeded to clear out the sink. 'The bits' looked like the uncooked scraps you might throw the dog after preparing the Sunday roast.

They were, apparently, bits of his patients that were no longer needed.

Despite criticism from the medical profession and even spiritualists, who regard his method of healing as not spiritual enough, Stephen Turoff perseveres with his mission. He attracts widespread media interest and co-operates with journalists and television reporters even though he knows that each new story will produce counter-claims and accusations. He even makes regular visits to Spain where the medical authorities have attempted to ban his unorthodox methods. But he is now known to an estimated 15 million Spaniards, thanks to the television discussion programme *Otra Dimension*, presented by Felix Gracia, which carried interviews with him and his spirit doctor as well as extensive coverage of healings. The sufferers he treated were clearly not in any pain, but it made for gruesome viewing.

One of the first to be treated was Isabel Duran from

Madrid who was blind in her left eye. After healing, however, she could see with that eye and was filmed reading a newspaper with the other eye covered. This led to claims by the sceptical medical profession and others that Stephen Turoff had paid the woman to pretend she had been blind. Those accusations of fraud continued until Isabel returned to the programme and held up medical records which proved that she had been blind in her left eye before receiving the psychic surgery treatment.

In addition to Dr Kahn, Stephen Turoff claims that Sai Baba, the Indian avatar, is a great influence on his work. And he also believes that the spirit of Brazilian psychic surgeon José Arigó has joined his team.

Wife prefers her husband's spirit surgeon

The healing work of another British medium, Ray Brown, is less controversial in some respects because he does not use any physical instruments to 'operate' on his patients. But his claim to be entranced by Paul of Judea, who was beheaded by the Romans for speaking out in support of Jesus, is regarded by some as name-dropping in the worst possible taste.

The former bricklayer's justification is that Paul was apparently a surgeon and now performs intricate surgery on the etheric or spirit bodies of his patients, producing remarkable cures without the need to open up their bodies, spill blood or remove diseased parts.

Writing about his unorthodox treatment of the sick in the *Daily Mail* (April 1998), Helen Carroll commented that the majority of those attending his Leicestershire clinic, where he sees several hundred people a month, 'make repeat appointments having experienced, it would appear, some relief from the treatment performed by Paul using "spiritual operating instruments" . . .'

There are, she adds, some noticeable differences between Ray, fifty-one, who is shy and short-sighted, and Paul who is confident, charming and witty, and manages perfectly well without glasses. 'Ray's accent wouldn't sound out of place on any building site,' she adds, 'but Paul's refined manner of talking, with a slight foreign lilt, is more suited to the Royal Enclosure at Ascot . . .'

Even Ray's wife of five years, Gillian, is said to prefer the personality of the spirit who controls her husband.

But not all healers have spirit doctors whose identities are conveniently shrouded in mystery or a lack of checkable detail.

Spirit doctor's identity confirmed by daughter

George Chapman has enjoyed a fifty-year association with the spirit of William Lang, a London ophthalmologist whose medical career can be checked by anyone prepared to make the effort. But those who have talked at length to 'Dr Lang', as he is known, through the body of his entranced medium, have discovered that his knowledge extends far beyond any facts which might be gleaned from medical archives.

At this point, I must declare an interest, for I have known Chapman and his spirit doctor for over thirty-five years and have collaborated with them on a number of books. I have done so because the evidence I have examined – both in terms of medical case studies and the continuing existence of William Lang beyond the grave – persuades me that this is not only a remarkable healing partnership but that it also provides us with some extremely strong evidence for life after death.

I confess that I first visited Chapman, when he was living in Aylesbury, with a more than healthy degree of scepticism. He had agreed to be interviewed and then go into trance so that I could also question William Lang. Towards the end of my talk with the spirit doctor, in his consulting room illuminated only by a dim red light, I realised that I would take away with me a wealth of fascinating information but no insight into how he conducted his spirit operations. Being healthy, I had no need for his help. So, instead, I asked for a 'check up'. Dr Lang happily obliged.

I climbed, fully clothed, onto the examination couch, as

thousands had done before me, and watched as he hunched over my body, his eyes tightly closed, and began snapping his fingers and moving his hands. He was, apparently, using various instruments to inspect and work on my etheric body which, it is claimed, is a 'mirror' of the physical body but formed of finer material, or vibrating at a different frequency (depending on which theory you subscribe to). If I were suffering from any imbalance or disease, say believers, it would show up in the etheric body and, by operating on that invisible counterpart, the benefit would transfer to my physical body. It sounded bizarre, and I was far from convinced, even though many patients had reported finding scars and other signs of surgery after undergoing a spirit operation. But then something happened which took my breath away.

The examination had been conducted systematically along my body and he had reached my head. He stopped and snapped his fingers, holding out his hand as if to take an instrument from an invisible helper. I watched intently as his hands hovered just inches above my face and his nimble fingers made the motions of cutting and probing. The cultured tones of Dr Lang (in marked contrast to the voice of Chapman which still betrays a Liverpudlian twang at times, despite not having lived in the North-West of England since his childhood) explained what he was doing. He had detected a weakness in my tear ducts. They were not causing me any problem at present and might not do so in the future. But, purely as a precautionary measure, he had decided to operate on them to keep them open and working properly.

Was this just a theatrical performance so that my story could also include a first-hand account of having an operation? Hardly. What Chapman could not have known was that, just a year or two before, my mother had gone into hospital to have an operation to overcome precisely the same problem. The tear duct in one of her eyes had degenerated to the point where it needed to be replaced by an artificial substitute. And her elder sister had had exactly the same operation a few years earlier. I have never met anyone else with this difficulty. It was clearly a genetic condition and Dr Lang had found it immediately. I must add that I have still not had any problem with my tear ducts.

Having been persuaded that something paranormal was going on here, I looked into the Chapman–Lang partnership in greater depth and wrote about it, in *Surgeon from Another World*, when I was finally at liberty to reveal some particularly important parts of the jigsaw. When Chapman first developed his mediumship and Dr Lang announced that he wanted to work with him in healing the sick, there were still a number of living people who had known Lang and could confirm or refute the claim.

Lang, a dapper, well-educated, refined man, had died in Sussex on 13 July 1937, when Chapman was just sixteen and embarking on a variety of manual jobs, including garage hand, butcher, docker and professional boxer in Liverpool. They were totally different. Yet, a few years later, the entranced Chapman was able to speak with Lang's mannerisms and hold long and intimate conversations with his friends and colleagues who had heard about his spirit return. Most were immediately convinced that Dr Lang had returned and they showed their acceptance and their support by giving Chapman articles which had once belonged to Lang. In time, Chapman's consulting room began to look very much like Lang's.

Then William Lang's only daughter, Lyndon, heard that a medium was claiming that the spirit of her father was working through him. Determined to expose the fraud, she arranged to visit Chapman's clinic, without revealing her identity. But William Lang recognised her immediately and, after a long discussion about things only the two of them knew, she was satisfied that Chapman was no fraud. Indeed, she gave him much support during her lifetime and left him a generous bequest in her will – as well as a statement confirming the authenticity of Dr Lang's spirit return.

Hundreds of cases of people being cured by Dr Lang have been published but he says the most important aspect of his work with George Chapman is to provide irrefutable evidence for life after death. Although now in his seventies and semi-retired, Chapman still sees patients at his clinic in Wales and regularly travels overseas so that Dr Lang can take his healing to as many people as possible.

It is, it seems, impossible to come to terms with spiritual healing without taking account of the very real possibility that the beneficial results are produced, at least in some cases, in association with the spirits of the dead.

8

SOUL DEEP

An American nurse named Anna had a weight problem. She had tried dieting, of course, but had reached the point where she felt she needed medical help. Leafing through the telephone directory's yellow pages Anna found the name of a psychiatric counsellor, Dr Robert Jarmon. A physician who had worked at a New Jersey hospital for eighteen years, having begun his career in emergency medicine, Dr Jarmon had also offered counselling for two decades.

After listening to Anna's problem, he asked if she was prepared to try hypnosis as a means of altering undesirable eating habits that were apparently leading to her weight gain. She readily agreed and appeared to be responding well to the therapy. But then, after two months, she complained of pain and tenderness in the right-lower quadrant of her abdomen and reported that she had stopped menstruating.

Anna asked Dr Jarmon if he could alleviate these symptoms but naturally his first concern was to determine their cause. He had been required to diagnose hundreds of cases of abdominal pain during his early career in emergency medicine and he knew that there were numerous possibilities, including an ovarian cyst, colitis, diverticulitis, appendicitis and even ectopic pregnancy in which the foetus develops in the fallopian tubes instead of the uterus. Dr Jarmon's tests proved negative, but, as Anna's abdomen became more swollen and tender, he insisted she saw her gynaecologist who diagnosed an ectopic pregnancy.

An operating room was hurriedly prepared for exploratory abdominal surgery and Anna was sent to the sonography lab to confirm the presence of either a foetus or something abnormal, such as a tumour. The test found nothing and the operation was cancelled.

Instead, Dr Jarmon used hypnosis to try to find the cause of his patient's puzzling condition.

'Go back now to where your problem started,' he suggested to the hypnotised Anna. 'Go back to where it began.'

She immediately held her side and began to moan. He asked her what was troubling her, and where and when this was happening.

'Long ago,' Anna answered. 'Long ago, not now, not here.'

Dr Jarmon was puzzled. What did she mean? Then, to his utter astonishment, she added: 'My name is Elizabeth.'

Under hypnosis, the New Jersey nurse had become someone else – a girl of nineteen who was experiencing great difficulty in the fifth month of pregnancy. She said a priest and a physician were at her bedside discussing her condition. The doctor wanted to remove the unborn child from her womb to save Elizabeth's life but the priest refused to let him do so because 'we cannot take life even to save a life'. The priest added: 'If God wills that the woman die, then she dies.'

Having conducted hundreds of hypnotic sessions with his patients over the years, Dr Jarmon had never experienced anything like this. Recalling Anna's first session, in his book *Discovering the Soul*, he tells us that, before that moment in time, he had no belief or interest in reincarnation, which he regarded as 'the stuff of fiction'. The transformation of Anna into Elizabeth changed that, particularly when she came out of trance and declared: 'My God! You finally did it, Dr Jarmon. I feel great. The pain is gone.' So, too, had the abdominal swelling and tenderness. Then, later that day, she phoned to say her period had started again, after an interval of five months.

Why had this happened?

Dr Jarmon explains that when he gave the instruction. 'Go back to where it began,' he meant in this life – because he had no belief in any other. But for his patient, Anna, it was an open invitation to search for the cause over many lifetimes – and in Elizabeth she found the answer.

Or perhaps her mind simply invented Elizabeth and the pregnancy as a way of explaining her abdominal pain.

Past-life therapy attacks the root cause

However we choose to interpret Anna's story, the fact is that it cured her of the mysterious pain. And it did so with remarkable speed. Having stumbled on a new use for hypnosis, Dr Jarmon was soon using past-life regression with other patients whose problems were not responding to more conventional treatments and finding it to be a very powerful therapeutic tool. Dr Edith Fiore, for example, insists, 'Other therapies address the symptoms and leave the cause untouched. Past-life therapy attacks the root cause. There isn't a single physical problem that can't be resolved by good past-life treatment.'

Many of those now using past-life therapy encountered it accidentally, like Dr Jarmon, during patient consultations. Instead of giving specific instructions, they 'allowed' their patients' minds the freedom to seek an answer from anywhere and any time, and were flabbergasted to hear their colourful, dramatic and often traumatic accounts which appeared to be memories of previous lives. Having done so, and watched the rapid improvement of their patients, these therapists are keen to use the technique again whenever they suspect a problem lies much deeper in the soul than the present lifetime.

Not all past-life therapists believe they are dealing with reincarnation. They see the reliving of past lives under hypnosis as yet further evidence of the mind's power to fantasise and invent in order to cure itself. They argue that it is unimportant whether they or their patients believe they have lived before; all that matters is that past-life therapy works.

Certainly, these hypnotic memories seldom provide verifiable information. They frequently sound like a good novel and in most cases they can be explained as cryptomnesia – the subconscious mind's ability to absorb a wealth of data acquired while reading or watching movies and television, then retrieve it long after the conscious mind has forgotten ever having seen it and 'dress it up' in a new and realistic guise. Others see past-life memories as metaphors.

Anarchist who 'went to pieces' dances again

'I don't hold a brief for reincarnation, though I am a firm believer,' says Roger Woolger, a Jungian psychologist and Oxford University graduate who now works mostly in the United States:

> I don't care whether you can prove it or whether you
> believe it or not. What is certain is that when the
> unconscious mind is given the opportunity to play
> stories *as if they are past lives* it comes up with
> staggering solutions, releases and spontaneous healings
> which you don't get in other therapies. So, as a
> pragmatist I've been drawn to past-life regression as a
> much more effective therapy than a lot of others.'

Woolger, whom I met on a visit to London, believes it isn't enough just to remember that your fear of water in this life was caused by drowning in a past life. You have to *relive* it in all its gruesome detail, he says, if your are to clear it from your system completely:

> To be effective you have to really go through it, you
> can't do it mentally – the body has to go through all the
> trembling and hysteria. We do a lot in our work to
> create a physical psychodrama, so if someone's trapped
> under a log or a fallen building, we have two people sit
> on them on a mattress so that the body has to feel the
> twists and contortions as it struggles out. In that way,

what I call the 'etheric memory' gets released, not just the mental and emotional memory of the event.

Some fears, he adds are very hard to release, particularly if they are associated with guilt. There are people who are trapped in self-blame, telling themselves 'I deserve to suffer' but without knowing why.

In his book *Other Lives, Other Selves*, he describes a striking case concerning a woman dancer, Edith, who had lupus erythematosus:

> This poorly understood non-infectious disease affects the immune system and produces many symptoms, including inflammation and cell damage. She had been a dancer but could no longer dance because she was in constant arthritic-like pain. She had tried all sorts of treatment, including holistic, but it seemed her limbs and the tissues between them were degenerating quite fast.
>
> She came to a workshop where we did some guided imagery work around the theme of warfare and the warrior, and she instantly found herself in a scenario at the turn of the century where she was a young Russian anarchist involved in a revenge bombing against the palace guard in what seems to be St Petersburg. I checked on this later, and there *was* an incident not unlike this.
>
> She found herself to be a survivor of the massacre going for revenge. And the story was that she was then a young man, about 18, avenging his father who'd been cut down a day or two before by the soldiers. He goes to throw a bomb into the barracks late at night and accidentally blows himself up instead. The next image is, 'I've gone, I'm not there,' and she went on with these terrible convulsions on the mat for the next half an hour and we just had to sit with them. What was most striking was all the shaking going on in her limbs; some tremendous release – I now call it 'etheric release' – of the bombing trauma.

At one point she said she was looking down at her body and I asked her what she saw. 'It doesn't have any arms and legs, the bomb blew my arms and legs off,' she replied. I asked her if the body was still alive and she said it was.

So I said, 'You're unfinished. You have to go back into your body,' and another round of trembling took place and finally I got her to the point where her body had released all the trauma, and I asked, 'What are your final, dying thoughts?' She replied, 'I'll never use my arms and legs again.'

That thought had imprinted with the trauma and was being revived in this incarnation.

Woolger says he does not know what triggered the lupus in this life, but imagines it has something to do with rage. But that session, which he describes as 'one of the most traumatic physical healings that I have seen take place' – proved to be a turning point for the woman. The pain began to disappear from her limbs and she slowly recovered and was able to dance once more.

You bring with you your dying thoughts

Though Woolger is not concerned about whether this was a real memory or a psycho-drama, there *are* past-life therapists who are adamant that their patients are remembering actual, previous lives, and who argue that these memories demonstrate that what we do in one life has a direct bearing on who we are and what we experience in the next. Indeed, the manner of our death in our last life and the thoughts we took to the grave may be having a totally unsuspected influence on our current existence.

Dr Morris Netherton, a pioneer of past-life regression, belongs to this school of thought. 'The unresolved trauma of death is a primary cause of behavioural disorder,' he maintains. 'Most of the problems I encounter have their source in past-life deaths. When the impact of these deaths is erased, many disorders simply evaporate.'

This is a view shared by Hazel Denning, who has been practising past-life therapy for well over forty years, was a founder of the Association for Past-Life Research and Therapy, and has done more than most to champion its use:

> I believe I was one of the first to realise that the last
> emotionally charged thought people have just as they
> are dying is the thought or emotion they bring with
> them into the next incarnation. Anger, resentment, fear,
> guilt – all seem to carry over and manifest even in very
> small children. 'I can't be trusted', I am going to get
> even with that . . .', 'Life is not fair', 'I am a bad person
> and need to be punished' are examples of the powerful
> energies that carry over and have to be dealt with in the
> current incarnation.

Patients always learn a spiritual lesson

Most past-life therapists agree that their clients gain much more than an improvement in their health as a result of recovering these memories.

'I believe that past-life regression therapy reaches more people and solves more problems faster than any other therapy because it gets to the primary cause and explains the whys,' says Hazel Denning. 'I never have a client that I don't ask, "What is the spiritual lesson for you in this experience? What is the purpose in this?" They always know.'

Indeed, one of Holland's most respected past-life therapists believes that it is a more thorough means of healing the sick than spiritual healing. According to Hans TenDam, in his book *Deep Healing*:

> Generally, spiritual healing is done too often and too
> quickly, especially by therapists who have more
> sensitivity than insight, therapists who love to help
> people. Healing is something like painting white a wall
> that has bubbles underneath, is dirty and greasy, and
> badly primed. At first sight the result is wonderful, but

three days later the first cracks emerge . . . Healing that
is full of goodwill and empty of method is sentimental
whitewashing.

Even Plato insisted, 'No attempt should be made to cure the
body without the soul.'

Whatever we may think about past-life therapy and the reasons why it appears to be such an effective healing method,
the fact remains that a belief in reincarnation may throw some
light on questions relating to our well-being which are seldom
answered satisfactorily by other belief systems.

Why are some people born with terrible deformities and
diseases – doomed to spend their lives in misery or agony?
Why are others blessed with good health, good looks and happiness? Even more relevant to the theme of this book, why are
some people instantly cured by healers, while others experience degrees of improvement and some are not helped at all?

The answer, many past-life therapists tell us, is to be found
in karma, the ancient belief in a universal law of cause and
effect. Though an Eastern concept, it is one which is increasingly being adopted by Western practitioners, influenced by
the growing popularity of Buddhism and meditation techniques. Many spiritual healers, though not past-life therapists, embrace karma and use it to help explain life's purpose
to their patients.

Healer lost his head in French Revolution

British healer Jack Angelo, for example, says he sometimes
looks at a patient with awe 'when I think of the total cosmic
journey this soul has already made'. He adds:

> Working with patients has convinced me that it is
> highly unlikely that a soul could experience all that it
> wishes to experience, learn all that it can learn and
> express all that it needs to express in the course of one
> lifetime. Secondly, where the law of cause and effect
> (karma) means that many of us leave the earth place

with an imbalance or experience to address, reincarnation gives us the chance to do this. If reincarnation is a fact, then karmic energies will be discovered in a patient's chakric system and will show up in the aura. This I have found to be the case.

Another British healer, David Furlong, who is also a founder tutor of the College of Healing and first chairman of the Natural Health Network, is also a believer. He tells of meeting a woman clairvoyant, when he was in his twenties, who told him she could see him, in a former life, being guillotined in the French Revolution. She added that this was why he suffered from tension headaches that stemmed from the back of his neck, which was true. This struck a chord with him for he had always felt uncomfortable when reading or watching films about the French Revolution. Later, while visiting Paris, he had a much more tangible feeling of having been there before in a previous life. He recalls:

> To lay to rest any difficult karma from that time, I felt it appropriate to send out thoughts of forgiveness in a symbolic sense to all who had caused me pain and suffering. This went well until I reached the Place de la Concorde, which is where the executions took place. Sitting quietly to send out these thoughts of forgiveness and healing I was suddenly struck by the thought, 'Why did I choose to be guillotined?' Like a bolt from the blue an immediate answer came back, 'Because you were responsible for cutting off other people's heads in an earlier life'. The power of this thought was so strong that I could not doubt its veracity.

To heal this situation, Furlong writes in *The Complete Healer* that he felt he had to ask forgiveness from any person he had similarly harmed, and that is what he did. Six months later he met a man on a healing course with whom a very strong interaction developed. That evening, the man regressed spontaneously to a life in China where he thought Furlong had been responsible for having his head cut off. They met a few days later and he told the healer about his experience, adding, 'I just want to say I forgive you.' Furlong comments: 'The power of that moment was electric.'

Notice that Furlong, as he sat in Paris, asked himself why he *chose* to be guillotined. Many believers in reincarnation assume that we all make choices about each life before we are born. Helped by our spirit guides and other wise masters, they say, we choose our parents, our friends and even our enemies, and we choose the difficulties we will encounter along the way, including perhaps sickness and how we will die. If that sounds fatalistic, most such belief systems also allow for a measure of free will. The idea is that in each life we build up a karmic debt which needs to be paid, and also karmic bonds with those we have loved. So, a parent in this life could have been a lover in a past life, or vice versa. If you wronged someone, you may also agree to find them in this life and ask forgiveness or help them in some way that wipes the slate clean. The same philosophical outlook can also be used to explain why you are rich or poor, healthy or sick, clever or stupid. Life is unfair . . . but only if we live just one life. If we have many lives, then the good and the bad balance out, and the unfairness of one life is more than compensated for by the good fortune of another.

Karma: not as simple as you might think

But who decides how these karmic laws work? Is a child who has been born crippled being punished for some dreadful deed committed in a former life? Or did he choose such an existence as part of his development or perhaps to teach others to be more understanding? The answer is, of course, that we cannot know. The more we try to unravel the mysteries of karma, the more we tie ourselves in knots.

To make matters even more complicated, a Welsh healer, Dave Cousins, assures me that there is physical karma, astral karma and mental karma. In addition, we each have personal karma, group karma, earth karma and solar system karma, not to mention positive and negative karma frequencies. Confused? I know I am. As the editor of a quarterly magazine on reincarnation, I would advise you to treat with caution anyone claiming to be able to read your karma, make judgements on the direction your soul has chosen, or determine the cause of any ailment from which you are suffering. That is something a good past-life therapist does not do. It is for the patient to draw his or her own conclusions from the memories which surface under hypnosis.

Dennis Barrett is also a healer who accepts that karma plays a vital role in shaping our lives. 'Parents have asked me why a particular illness has struck their child,' he explains. 'Why couldn't it have happened to them instead? I explain that we cannot take on someone else's lessons. There is an experience for the child in coping with the illness and quite a different one in their caring for the child. Both experiences are important to the spirits involved.'

There are, of course, numerous reasons why people become ill. Some abuse their bodies with alcohol and drugs. Others take no exercise or push themselves to the limit, resulting in stress. Then there are those who carry anger or hatred around inside them, poisoning their bodies without realising it. Any healing that is going to be effective has to do more than treat the symptoms. A chain-smoker who continues smoking after receiving healing for his lungs is unlikely to experience any improvement that lasts very long. But perhaps we should not look at health in terms of this life only. Maybe the time has come to take a broader view of healing, as suggested by past-life therapists, and allow for the possibility that success in treating patients may sometimes be determined by actions in their previous lives which need addressing in this one.

9

HEALING YOURSELF

As we saw in Chapter Four, the mind, particularly under hypnotic suggestion, can produce some startling changes in the human body, and the placebo effect has been credited with being as powerful as some drugs. So, shouldn't we be learning from these discoveries and applying them to our lives in order to enjoy good health and even cure ourselves if we do get sick? This is a view that is being discussed by more and more medical professionals as they explore the evidence that the mind–body relationship plays a more important part in our well-being than many had thought possible.

Before we take a look at these exciting findings in greater depth, it is important to stress that you will find no one working on mind–body studies and their implications for self-healing who advocates that we should turn our backs on medical science. When you are sick you need the advice of a medical expert who can diagnose your problem and suggest a remedy. But, as we shall see, this can be just part of the answer. Those who also have a greater understanding of the way the mind controls the body, and the power of belief and suggestion in restoring us to good health, are likely to enjoy faster results. They may even have the satisfaction of proving the medical prognosis wrong.

It is well known that some illnesses do go into remission

for varying periods of time. What is not so widely known is that, throughout history, there have been cases of people who suddenly get completely better for reasons that are a complete mystery to them, their associates, and the doctors or physicians treating them. The speed with which such cures often occur just adds to the mystery, although science is beginning to discover some of the mechanisms which might be at work. Such 'miracle healings' hold out the hope that it might eventually be possible for us all to harness the inner power that achieves such transformations.

Spontaneous remissions from cancer

In fact, the patron saint of cancer sufferers, St Peregrine, was a thirteenth-century cancer victim who experienced a spontaneous remission. Then a Roman Catholic monk, Peregrine Laziosi developed a leg tumour for which the only 'cure' was amputation. The night before the drastic operation was due to be carried out, the monk prayed for help and then dreamed that he had been cured. The next morning the tumour was gone. He lived to the age of eighty, dying in 1345 after devoting the rest of his life to the relief of suffering in others. He was canonised by the Catholic Church in 1726.

Over thirty-five years ago, Dr Charles Mayo, a surgeon at Minnesota's Mayo Clinic, operated on a 63-year-old woman with cancer of the colon, which had spread to nearby lymph nodes and both lobes of her liver. The surgery could not possibly cure the disease but was carried out in order to provide the patient with temporary relief from some of the more unpleasant symptoms from which she was suffering. He did not tell her she had cancer, but warned her family she would live no more than nine months.

That was in May 1950. Some twelve years later, in 1962, the clinic received a letter from the woman's son. 'Since five years without recurrence of a cancer is considered a cure,' he wrote, 'could it be that this was a case of self-cure, about which I have read several reports?'

Dr Mayo, astonished to learn that his patient was still alive, arranged for her to be brought into the hospital. Her physical and X-ray examinations, blood count and blood chemistry revealed no evidence of cancer.

What had caused the remarkable spontaneous remission? Dr Mayo, as mystified as most other medical men would be in the circumstances, wrote that 'one can only speculate', adding, 'To understand the basis of such cures would be to gain fundamental knowledge about the control of malignant growths and the host–tumour relationship.'

And yet very little effort has been made to study spontaneous remissions. Some have suggested that partial surgeries or other medical treatments may somehow trigger a full recovery. Others believe that mental processes bring about the curative chemical and immune changes. There is also evidence that those who enjoy such remissions usually experience life-changing events shortly before the cure – anything from a religious conversion to reconciliation with someone or even a sudden marriage.

Charles Weinstock, a psychiatrist and professor at the Albert Einstein College of Medicine in New York for example, studied eighteen consecutive cases from his own practice and found that in all of them, the remission had been preceded by 'favourable psycho-social change' within one to three weeks. Dr Yujiro Ikemi, of the Department of Psychosomatic Medicine at Kyushu University in Japan, discovered life changes in five Japanese cases of spontaneous remission, observing that this dramatic change of outlook on life 'seemed to have led to the full activation of their innate self-recuperative potentials'.

While these studies shed light on important psychological influences, they do not explain the physical mechanism that rids the body of such diseases. In fact, spontaneous remissions may not be as rare as we imagine, and an understanding of how they occur could have tremendous importance for the whole of medicine.

'No condition is quite hopeless'

Two physicians, Tilden Everson and Warren Cole, began a survey of medical literature in the 1960s, searching for cases of spontaneous remission from cancer in American medical journals over a sixty-year period. They disregarded types of cancer which can routinely go into remission and also ignored those cases which were diagnostically suspect. Even so, they still collected 176 cases in which doctors confirmed that a cancer had regressed either without treatment, or after treatment that theoretically should not have helped.

More recently, the Institute of Noetic Studies carried out a far more extensive study, covering 830 medical journals in over twenty languages. It found 3500 accounts of spontaneous remission, from a case involving a breast tumour in 1846, to reports published in the 1990s. Excerpts from these accounts were published in the Institute's *Spontaneous Remission – An Annotated Bibliography* in 1993. This study shows that in 15 per cent of cases remission occurred without therapeutic drugs or treatment. In other cases, although partial or palliative surgeries or treatments had been given, they should not – in theory – have produced cures. Spontaneous remission was reported from almost every disease, including every form of cancer.

One case involved a 31-year-old Baltimore woman who was a patient of Sir William Osler (1814–1919), best-known as the author of the medical textbook *The Principles and Practice of Medicine* (1892). Sir William sailed to England in June 1890 after examining a patient on whom he had originally operated to remove her right breast which had been found to be cancerous. Shortly before his departure, she consulted him again. She now had pains in her back and leg, vision difficulties in her right eye, a new growth in her left breast, and a mass of tumour that rose directly from the centre of her chest. There was nothing he could do, apart from giving her morphine to ease the pain, and she was soon confined to her bed. As he sailed for England he never expected to see her again. But eighteen months later, on his return to

America, she met him at the railway station. Her pain and the lump on her chest had completely gone. 'She had improved in every way,' he observed, which led him to the conclusion 'that no condition, however desperate, is quite hopeless.'

But what had happened to bring about the change?

A more recent report from the Institute of Noetic Sciences collection, the case of 59-year-old Peggy McNeil, a southern Texas housewife who discovered she had cancer in 1983, gives us a clue. A biopsy on a swollen lymph node, carried out by doctors at the Valley Diagnostic Clinic in Harlingen, showed it to be badly affected by large-cell carcinoma, a kind of cancer. Other tests showed a large tumour on her right lung, from which cancer had already spread to the lymph node and was likely to migrate throughout her body. She was told that it was not possible to operate on such a tumour and that she had only eight months to live.

Chemotherapy and radiation treatments were likely to sap her energy and deny her valuable time. She had a lot to do and not much time to do it in, so she refused treatment and went home to die. A decade later, however, Peggy McNeil was still alive and X-rays showed no signs of the disease. Somehow, her resolve to stay in control seems to have defeated the cancer. When we begin to examine such cases, we find there are many successful self-healing techniques which do not involve anything more than the power of the mind.

The man who laughed himself better

American journalist Norman Cousins took literally the old saying, 'Laughter is the best medicine,' or, to quote a more ancient version. 'A merry heart doeth good like a medicine'. Stricken by an often fatal degenerative disease of the spine, ankylosing spondylitis, he had been put on four different medications to relieve the pain and inflammation. His doctor held out little hope of recovery.

However, Cousins had been a medical journalist earlier in his career and was aware of emerging evidence that pessimism and depression could reduce the body's resistance to disease. On that basis, he told himself, a positive attitude should increase resistance and perhaps overcome sickness. With his doctor's co-operation he stopped most of his medication, ordered large doses of vitamin C, which he believed would help counteract the inflammation, and then started having positive thoughts – and lots of laughs. 'Nothing is less funny than being flat on your back with all the bones in your spine and joints hurting,' he wrote, in his bestselling book about his fight against the disease, *Anatomy of an Illness*. A movie projector and screen were placed in his room and he fed himself a regular diet of old Marx Brothers' films and episodes of TV's *Candid Camera*. Another treatment of his own devising was for nurses to read to him from humorous books.

'I made the discovery that ten minutes of genuine belly laughter had an anaesthetic effect and would give me at least two hours of pain-free sleep,' Cousins wrote. Noting this effect, Cousins' doctor decided to sample his blood sedimentation rate – a crucial measure of inflammation – before and after each laugh session. He found that it fell slightly with each one, and continued to fall as Cousins gradually recovered.

By 1976 Cousins was ready to reveal his unorthodox cure in the *New England Journal of Medicine*, raising many eyebrows and an occasional smile within the medical community. We now know that his was not an isolated case. Other research has shown that laughter not only reduces stress and eases pain, but also seems to alter the body stress and immunity chemistry. For example, in one study, ten healthy subjects had blood samples taken at ten-minute intervals. Half of them sat quietly for an hour. The others watched a sixty-minute videotape of a famous comedian. When their respective blood samples were tested for eight different hormones and biochemical messengers, it was found that members of the group who watched the comedy show experienced a significant drop in cortisol and epinephrine, two stress hormones that are known to decrease immune function.

Fighting cancer with the mind

Just a few years before Cousins published his story, a young radiologist, Carl Simonton, revealed the results of some pioneering medical research he had conducted at Travis Air Force Base in California. Speaking at the Dimensions of Healing symposium at the University of California, Los Angeles, in 1972, Simonton explained how he had wondered whether the visualisation techniques he used in meditation could be adopted by patients as a healing force. He and others had noticed that the very small number of terminally ill cancer patients who managed to survive appeared to be well-motivated and intent on exerting some control over the course of their disease.

Simonton, who had trained at the University of Oregon Medical School as a cancer specialist with a sub-specialty in radiation, was in charge of the radiation department at the base hospital. Suspecting that visualisation could enable more cancer sufferers to fight the disease, he managed to get permission to try his method on patients considered to be beyond medical help. He presented slides at the symposium – of rectal, mouth and various other types of cancer in advanced stages, and then showed photographs of the same patients after they had tried his technique. The improvement astonished many.

His method of treatment, which he called 'focused relaxation', was simply to ask his patients, and sometimes their relatives, to visualise what needed to happen in order for their health to return. They were instructed to do this for a certain period each day. The first 'guinea pig' had a tumour in his throat. He was told to visualise his own body defences at work during three-fifteen minute sessions each day, and also to picture the tumour diminishing in size. He had to exclude all other thoughts during this exercise. The tumour disappeared and did not return. With other cancer patients the recovery rate was also high.

There were extreme reactions – both favourable and unfavourable – from many of his colleagues when Simonton first presented his evidence that the mind could have an impact on cancer. He and his wife, Stephanie, a motivational psychologist, published the results of their studies in a best-selling book *Getting Well Again*, in which they reported treating 159 'incurable' cancer patients, all of whom had been given just a year to live. Most lived at least twenty months and about a quarter recovered partially or completely from the disease.

Patient's mental Pacman 'eats' cancer cells

Among those who read the book and followed its advice was 56-year-old Doris Phillips. In 1982 she was told by Dr James Suen of the University of Arkansas Medical Centre that her throat cancer had now spread to her lungs. Dr Suen is a prominent throat specialist who has treated President Bill Clinton's recurring laryngitis. Mrs Phillips had undergone two major operations and thirty radiation treatments over the previous twenty years in her battle against adednocystic carcinoma, a slow-growing but inexorably recurring form of cancer. Dr Suen suggested chemotherapy which might temporarily shrink the lung tumours but would not cure them. Mrs Phillips decided instead to put her affairs in order and prepare to die. Not surprisingly, she suffered from overwhelming depression during this time and turned for help to a counsellor, who presented her with a copy of *Getting Well Again*. She decided, at once, to follow the Simontons' techniques and it proved to be a turning point in her life.

Several times a day she would retreat to the quiet of her bedroom and visualise her body fighting the cancer. Her imagery was ingenious. She saw the 'good' cells in her body gobbling up the cancer cells like a Pacman video game, and even obtained a copy of her chest X-ray so she could pinpoint the tumours' exact location to help her kill them. Then she called her children to announce that she was not going to die. 'I quit being happy with my illness,' she explained. 'I quit calling it "my cancer". Of course, it was hard at the beginning. I missed seeing the sad looks on people's faces when I told them I had cancer. If the subject did come up I would say, "Back when I had cancer".'

Mrs Phillips had not told Dr Suen what she was doing and, certain that she was improving, was disappointed to learn from him, during her regular check-up a few months later, that her cancer 'had not got any worse'. She determined to put even greater effort into her self-healing programme and increased the number and length of her visualisation periods. On her next visit to Dr Suen she knew immediately he had seen her latest X-rays. 'He came in with a strange look on his face,' she recalled. 'He asked me what I had been doing and showed me that the tumours were all gone. He asked a million questions.' A decade later, Doris Phillips was still well and free from cancer.

A similar research project to Dr Carl Simonton's was conducted in the 1990s by clinical psychologist Dr Leslie Walker at Aberdeen Royal Infirmary, Scotland. Half the group were given relaxation therapy for three weeks while the others were not. Announcing their results in July 1997, he said cancer patients who had been taught to picture themselves battling their tumours had showed changes in their immune system. At this stage the researchers did not know if it was the fighting aspect of the visualisation or the relaxation therapy which made the difference, he said, 'but a key factor they may have in common is that they both encourage patients to be more in control of their feelings moment by moment.'

How to ignore statistics and labels

Not everyone finds it so easy to visualise their body fighting against disease, particularly if their medical knowledge tells them it is an impossible task. Dr Deepak Chopra, the New England endocrinologist and guru of self-healing, tells the story of a middle-aged radiologist who had been diagnosed with leukaemia.

'He was extremely sophisticated in his knowledge of the disease, an unpredictable form called chronic myelogenous leukaemia, meaning that it affected the white blood cells called myelocytes,' Dr Chopra explains in his book *Quantum Healing*. There were few signs yet of the disease, apart from some fatigue during the day, but the patient knew the average survival period, from the onset of the disease, was thirty-six to forty-four months. However, because it is unpredictable, he might live much longer. Specialists at the leading cancer institute in New York City had offered him a choice of half a dozen experimental drug protocols. Again, he knew that there was no single accepted treatment for his leukaemia and that none of the experimental ones he had been offered came with any promises of an extended life expectancy.

He rejected treatment and, instead, began reading everything he could find on spontaneous remissions. He came across something Dr Chopra had written and sought him out for that reason.

As they talked, Dr Chopra became aware of a huge stumbling block.

'I want to believe I will recover from this,' the radiologist told him, 'but something really worries me. I read about a lot of remissions from cancer, but I didn't run across any spontaneous remissions from leukaemia.'

Furthermore, the type of leukaemia from which he was suffering is linked to a genetic component, called the Philadelphia chromosome, and he had tested positive for this.

'Being a physician, that was the end of the story – he was genetically marked for doom.'

No matter how hard Dr Chopra tried to persuade his patient that he could beat the disease, it was clear that his mind believed it was impossible. But then Dr Chopra had an idea.

'Why don't you tell yourself you have some other cancer,' he suggested. 'Then at least you would have hope for a remission.'

The man leaped at the suggestion. He was also encouraged by a review article Chopra showed him which connected childhood leukaemia and stress. Although his was a totally different disease, he *was* leading an incredibly stressful life which included having 'to support two houses and three Mercedes'. Indeed, it was during his rancorous divorce that the diagnosis had been made.

Since then, the man appears to be making good progress in his battle against leukaemia, which his mind is prepared to fight on the basis that it is cancer.

'So far,' Dr Chopra writes, 'I have done nothing for this man except change the label on his disease, but from that he changed his whole appraisal. Now we have a chance to witness the birth of a cure.'

Imagining you have a different disease to the one you really have may sound bizarre, but there is growing evidence that this sort of mind trick is exactly what is needed to accomplish healing transformations.

Brain scans provide a vital clue

In 1996, Dr Herbert Benson, Associate Professor of Medicine at Harvard Medical School and author of *The Relaxation Response*, told a London conference about the work of a colleague, Stephen Cozlitt. He had carried out positron emission tomography (PET) scans on subjects, and his findings have an important bearing on our understanding of the placebo effect, Dr Herbert told delegates at The Placebo Response: The Biology of Belief conference held at the University of Westminster. A PET scan enables doctors to watch what is going on in a living brain. As Dr Benson explained, Stephen Cozlitt:

> . . . showed them, let's say, a letter 'A' on a grid and did a PET scan. This showed that a certain area of their visual cortex was active, and represented what their brain was doing as it looked at the letter 'A'. Next, he had them close their eyes, then open them and look at a plain grid, and told them in their mind's eye to visualise the letter 'A' – in other words they were not actually seeing it. And he did another PET scan. Exactly the same area lit up – they were indistinguishable.

The obvious conclusion to be drawn from this research, according to Dr Benson, was that 'from the brain's point of view, whether you are *looking* at the letter "A", or *thinking* of the letter A, it is the same. It is a reality for the brain.'

So, it is not too big a jump to conclude that, if you *imagine* your body to be healthy, and you visualise it strongly enough, it becomes your brain's reality and it sends out the necessary messages to your body so that you return to good health.

How the body can be tricked

Dr Benson also told delegates of Dr Stuart Wolfe's experiments in the 1950s, in which the subjects were pregnant women suffering from nausea and vomiting. After asking them to swallow small gastric balloons in order to measure the contractions of their stomachs, he confirmed that the characteristic waves of nausea and vomiting were present. He then gave them something to stop these and confirmed that their stomachs had returned to normal. In fact, what Dr Wolfe had given them was not a substance that stopped nausea and vomiting but syrup of ipacac which *causes* these conditions. It is sometimes given to young patients who have swallowed a dangerous substance in order to induce vomiting. But, because the patients believed it would cure them, their minds not only rid their bodies of the symptoms but also *reversed* the drug's pharmacological action. These tests, Dr Benson pointed out with a smile, were conducted in the days before human studies committees.

In the UK, tests were carried out in which subjects were told the substance they were given would cause nasal constriction. Sure enough, they had asthma attacks. They were then told they would be given something that would prevent an asthma attack when taken before they were given the offending substance. As predicted, once they had taken the new concoction, the asthma attack was prevented. In fact, what they were given both to induce the asthma attack and prevent it was exactly the same ... distilled water.

In a Japanese study, students known to be allergic to the wax of a lacquer tree (similar to poison ivy) were blindfolded. Then they were informed that their left arms would be stroked with a chestnut tree leaf and their right arms with a lacquer tree leaf. Their left arms showed no reaction to the stroking but their right arms, as expected, broke out in a full-blown rash. It was only at the end of the experiment that they were told the leaves had been reversed. Their belief and expectancy had produced the rash on their right arms, just as it had totally eliminated their allergic reaction to the lacquer leaves that brushed their left arms.

These are all examples of the placebo effect, a phrase Dr Herbert Benson prefers not to use because the term now has a pejorative connotation – 'it's all in the mind', 'it's just your imagination', 'it's the placebo effect'. Instead, he likes to talk about 'remembered wellness'. Norman Cousins, the journalist who laughed his way back to good health, calls it 'the chemistry of the will to live'.

Mind–body relationship dominates medicine

In a study carried out by Henry Beecher, the first Professor of Anaesthesiology at Harvard Medical School, the placebo effect was found to be at work in almost a third of all cases in which patients consult doctors. It even starts *the moment* they call the doctor: just knowing they have an appointment with someone who they believe can make them better frequently changes their condition. The 30 per cent statistic has now been revised upward, says Dr Benson. We now know that 60 to 90 per cent of visits to doctors in Britain, Europe and the United States are concerned with mind–body, stress-related ailments.

There are, of course, many ways of treating such problems. Encouraging patients to relax, meditate, take more exercise, change their attitudes and their bad habits, and improve their diet may all be part of a recommended cure. But ultimately, it seems, we all have the power to heal ourselves, so long as we believe strongly enough that we can do it. But it is not easy, as Dr Benson explains in his new book *Timeless Healing: the power of biology and belief*:

> We harangue ourselves for not being perfect, for not living life with the panache portrayed in magazines or on TV. We adulate the firm-bodied, we exercise like zealots or wallow in guilt if we don't, choosing diet shakes over moderation . . . We aspire to parent perfectly, to juggle flawlessly the demands of work and home, and to have marriages and relationships of unwavering passion . . . In this climate, it's very hard to remember wellness.

He goes on to offer his own ideas on reversing negative patterns and, in particular, on modifying our addiction to pre-programmed information designed to manipulate us for commercial purposes.

But we are still left with the question: how does the brain achieve self-healing, ridding us of tumours, skin diseases and a host of other afflictions?

What goes on in the mind–body relationship to bring about such miracles?

Super computer in our heads

Inside our heads is an incredibly sophisticated super computer consisting of 100 billion cells, each with a body, a nucleus and branches that carry impulses in and out. The branches from each cell are just like those on a tree, making smaller and smaller twigs with anywhere between 5000 and 500,000 endings.

The miracle of this incredible structure is that the twigs can all communicate with each other and are constantly exchanging information by electrical impulses through what are known as neurotransmitters which convey the 'message' down the line until it reaches its destination.

As if that were not complicated enough, it transpires that there are at least sixty neurotransmitters which can send a signal in any one of ten different strengths. This means that at any given moment the number of messages being processed by the brain is in the range of two to the hundredth trillion power. So, says Dr Benson. 'Every single thought you have; every emotion you feel, every motion you make is a result of these neurotransmitters communicating moment by moment.'

It seems reasonable to assume, then, that some illnesses or imbalances are caused by the brain reacting in some way to messages it receives, whether in response to our own mis-treatment of our bodies or our own self-deprecation (may be due to guilt or stress, or even illusion). What the evidence of healing, hypnosis and spontaneous remission suggests is that we do not have to accept that situation. Our brains are only doing what they are programmed to do, but it seems we have the power to re-program or override them – to cause the neu-rotransmitters to carry their messages to different cells or even block the messages – in order to restore our health.

Inner voice gives accurate diagnosis

But *who* is in control? Is the mind a product of the brain or its master? Do we each have a guiding intelligence – or soul – which ultimately governs these activities? Put another way, are we just the sum total of our brain's fantastic capabilities, a body dictated to by a brain; or is the brain merely a sophis-ticated computer which we use to keep body and soul together?

Before you consider these questions, let me share one more extraordinary story of self-healing with you, reported in the December 1997 issue of the *British Medical Journal*, involv-ing a woman with a history of psychological problems. One day, sitting at home, she heard a voice in her head which told her not to be afraid: it, and a friend, wanted to help her. Concerned, she sought medical help and Ikechukwu Azuonye, a consultant psychiatrist who treated her, said she appeared to be cured after receiving medication and coun-selling. She was well enough to take a holiday, but while abroad the voices came back and urged her to return immediately to England, which she did. Back in London, the voices gave her an address to go to. She followed their instructions and found herself outside the brain scan department of a large London hospital.

On arrival, the voices told her to go in and ask to have a brain scan, as she had a tumour in her brain. To reassure her, Mr Azuonye explains in his report to the prestigious medical journal, he arranged for her to have a scan even though there was no sign of her having a tumour. But the results revealed that she did, indeed, have a tumour. After a successful operation to remove it, she reported hearing the voices once more. They told her: 'we are pleased to have helped you. Goodbye.'

She has since made a full recovery.

10
HEALING ANIMALS

Though we humans can practise techniques that will help us heal ourselves, animals are not so fortunate. Their health generally depends on the care we give them and the expertise of the veterinary surgeons we consult when they are unwell. But there is no reason why we should not consider healing for the animals in our lives – particularly as all the evidence points to them being very responsive subjects. What is more, those cases where healing produces dramatic results also furnish us with further evidence that there is much more to the laying-on-of-hands than the placebo effect. After all, animals, we assume, are not likely know the difference between a veterinary surgeon and a healer, yet the latter can often produce results when the former can do no more.

Healed unintentionally

One of English healer Matthew Manning's patients at his Cambridgeshire sanctuary was a woman who was devoted to her dog, a long-haired dachshund. The pet had injured its back by jumping off a wall, leaving it incontinent and its back legs paralysed. An X-ray showed that the discs in its spine were out of alignment and a veterinary surgeon who examined the dachshund recommended that it be put down. His owner, however, refused to be parted from her pet and instead did everything to make the animal's existence as comfortable as possible.

When she consulted Manning, she did not want to leave the dog unattended. Instead, she picked him up and put him on her knee while Manning gave healing. He did not touch the dog nor think much about it during the healing session. His healing focus was entirely on his human patient. Yet, next morning, the woman was overwhelmed to find that her dog was better. His back legs were no longer paralysed and when she took him to the vet, he confirmed that the discs were now aligned. Puzzled by this totally unexpected cure, he could offer no explanation.

W.C. Fields said, 'Never work with animals or children' – advice he gave, tongue-in-cheek, to other performers. But it is not followed by healers who usually find both make very good patients. Manning points out that he and other UK healers are not allowed to treat animals under the Veterinary Surgeons Act of 1966, without reference to a vet. Nevertheless, there are a number of healers who make animals their speciality, but they check that they have been seen by a vet first.

Alsatian healed on television

The British are well-known animal lovers, so it is not altogether surprising to find that UK healers dominate in treating all creatures great and small. And whenever television directors want to feature healing, they often win viewer sympathy by finding a four-legged sufferer to be the patient. In *The Paranormal World of Paul McKenna*, the well-known hypnotist introduced viewers to Sasha, an Alsatian dog suffering from chronic arthritis, and two skin problems – ulcers and acute eczema. Her owners had considered having her put to sleep because she was suffering so much pain. Instead, they agreed to let healer Malcolm Bessant treat her. He spent half an hour with her, on three occasions, holding his hands over the areas affected. Part of the treatment was filmed by the TV cameras.

Sasha's owners reported a definite improvement. Her skin conditions were visibly improved and she was clearly suffering less pain from the arthritis after these treatments. But what they noticed most was the psychological change.

'I took her for a walk and she was a different dog – lively, running ahead of me – whereas before I'd been almost dragging her along,' said one of her owners. 'Her old interest had come back. I have to say that it was remarkable. But I can't explain it.'

Explaining animal healing is difficult for everyone involved – particularly vets who see their patients, for whom they could do no more, made well by unqualified and unorthodox practitioners. Yet there is no denying the evidence. In fact, it is powerful enough to persuade some vets to work with healers.

Healer works alongside vet

Richard Allport, who qualified as a vet in 1973, runs a practice just north of London, at Potter's Bar, in Hertfordshire. It was the beneficial healing which his wife, an occupational health nurse, received for a back condition from a colleague which opened his mind to healing. Soon afterwards he heard about the work of animal healer Charles Siddle. He investigated for himself and was impressed. Now Siddle runs a weekly clinic at Allport's practice, treating his and other vets' patients.

'I know what he's doing, but I don't know how he does it,' Allport confesses;

There is no doubt that he has healed and helped to heal many of my patients and patients referred from other practices. My own feeling is that healing is some sort of energy transfer and Charles is a sort of conductor. But what the energy consists of and whether one could measure it, I don't know. All I know is that it works and it's safe. I am not saying that it is going to be a cure-all, but I think it can help.

The white-bearded healer certainly employs unusual techniques to produce his remarkable results, as he travels round
attending a wide variety of sick creatures. The humans who
call him in are often sceptical when they see him produce a
large white crystal and place it near the animal. And they are
similarly surprised at the speed with which the treatment
takes place and the certainty he expresses that the patient will
get better.

Siddle talks incessantly as he treats his patients, which his
human clients assume is his way of reassuring the animals. In
fact, he explains, he is really in conversation with the spirit of
the late Buster Lloyd Jones, a famous vet who died in 1980 and
was a believer in healing. It is Buster who tells him what to do
and confirms that the patient will benefit from the healing.
Apparently, Buster's spirit returned in a stable one day and said
he wanted to do healing and would work through Siddle. Now,
when the healer is asked to treat a sick animal, Buster's spirit
goes ahead to check it out so that by the time Siddle arrives a
diagnosis has been made and the healing can start immediately.

Showjumper makes rapid recovery

Among those who have benefited from this two-world partnership is Orion Blaze, a £40,000 showjumper who went
lame after tearing muscles in one of his forelegs. After one
treatment from Siddle, Orion Blaze made a remarkably quick
recovery. Another successful equine patient was Jessica, one
of many horses in Jan Piper's stables. By 1992 she had given
birth to two race-winning foals and was expected to produce
more. Then she became sick and vet Mark Sinnott discovered
she was suffering from equine lymphosarcoma, a type of
white cell cancer.

'This condition has an extremely poor prognosis,' the vet
explains. 'Horses usually deteriorate quite rapidly, and there
is no known cure for this form of cancer. Chemotherapy may
be a potential treatment in the future, but at the moment once
the diagnosis is made the horse usually ends up having to be
put to sleep.'

Despite their scepticism, Jan and her husband Graham called in Charles Siddle. They had nothing to lose. The very next morning Jessica had changed dramatically. Stablehand Mandy Drummond found her bright-eyed and active. She had eaten all her hay and was calling and kicking at the door for food.

From that moment on, Jessica's health returned to normal and many of the lumps faded within a couple of weeks. Three years later she was still fighting fit and has had another foal which also looks like becoming a winner.

'Jessica has never looked back and, as a result, my attitude towards healing has completely changed,' says Jan Piper. 'I did not believe one little bit in it. It would never have entered my head to use a healer. Now I wouldn't hesitate. If anything happened to any of the horses I'd phone Charles straightaway. It's a miracle. Really, I cannot explain why she is still alive.'

The vet who diagnosed Jessica's condition says, 'I discussed her case with other vets and they are of the opinion that no horse has ever recovered from equine lymphosarcoma. By all the laws of veterinary medicine Jessica should be dead by now, but she's still walking around happily in the field with a foal. This is something that we cannot explain.'

And vet Richard Allport, similarly puzzled by such recoveries, comments: 'I would say that animals do not experience a placebo effect. They cannot imagine that they are going to get better. So if the animals respond – and in my experience they do – then it must be a real healing effect.'

'Horse charmer' realigns bones

Horses feature prominently in accounts of animal healers. But that's no surprise in the case of Sussex-based John Harland, for his extraordinary rapport with them has resulted in him being labelled a 'horse charmer'. Writing in the *Daily Mail Weekend* in May 1997, Colin Dunne told of his meeting with Harland in the stables of Elaine Barter at Lower Beeding, West Sussex, where he had been called to treat Hagar, the first foal Elaine had bred herself. Hagar was now suffering from weak hindquarters and a back so tender he could not bear the weight of a saddle.

Grey-haired and bearded, Harland had been a farrier for forty years before discovering his talent. After hearing Hagar's problems, he observed, 'Not symmetrical, that's the trouble with them all.' Then, in Dunne's words, he began 'his performance, at once comical, eerie and incongruous'. Standing next to the horse, he kept his left hand still while his right hand circled in front of Hagar's nose.

'Ooh, yes. I can feel my fingers tingling now,' the 57-year-old healer said. 'Then sometimes it comes in a huge surge.' He told the journalist that his hands move of their own accord and 'I'll swear they spark in the dark'.

Harland then predicted that the horse's nose would twitch, his muscles move and he would yawn and become sleepy. This all happened as he said it would. Hagar's problem, he explained, was that the structure of his body had gone out of shape. His explanation for this was that the 'electromagnetic field around the horse and the electrical impulses inside are not compatible' and had therefore distorted his body. But the horse charmer has the power to realign every bone and muscle and that is what he did for Hagar, who soon showed his appreciation by galloping around a field 'in a dance of celebration'.

Two weeks later, Colin Dunne returned to check on Hagar's progress. He was, he reported, positively frisky. But had he actually changed shape, as Harland said he needed to?

Elaine Barter insists that he had. 'His backside, which was flat, is now nice and round, he doesn't stand with his two front legs underneath him any more and his shoulders have lined up.' And she adds: 'I don't know if it's electromagnetism, hypnotism or what. All I know is that it works.'

Harland discovered this power six years earlier while working with an equine osteopath. At first he used laying-on-of-hands but then found he did not need to touch the horses to heal them.

He treats about twenty horses a week for a modest fee and is in great demand. A chauffeur-driven car whisked him off to

Newmarket on one occasion so that he could treat six valuable race horses. And many of Harland's clients were happy
to tell the journalist their stories of the miraculous improvements they had witnessed.

A Welsh cob belonging to Patricia Galletly, from
Laughton, near Lewes, for example, was stable-bound with
maminitis. There was nothing the vet could do for Taffy and
the whole family was in tears. Now, after treatment from
Harland, Taffy is jumping and eventing once again. And
another of her horses, a 31-year-old hunter named Cossack,
behaves like a two-year-old instead of an old age pensioner.
'John is blessed with something,' she states. 'He made him
young again – I wish he'd do the same for me.'

He does not limit his healing work to animals. 'In one
house, John treated the horse, the owner and the dog,' Dunne
wrote. 'If he'd included the budgerigar, no one would have
been in the least surprised. And yes, he did my back too – a
post-squash problem – as we stood by the gate overlooking
the horses in the valley. Afterwards, I didn't actually gallop
round the field, but I knew exactly how Hagar felt. Better.'

Pet cat helped her healing talent to develop

For Devon healer Nicky Prouvost, whose healing of animals
has also been featured on TV, there is no mystery about her
healing gift. Born in France, Prouvost did not discover her
power until moving to England and caring for her own cat.
When the pet responded rapidly to the healing, Prouvost's
friends began bringing their animals to her for treatment.
Now she runs her Pets Healing Clinic at Totnes and has many
grateful clients who testify to her healing powers – and just as
many patients who would do the same if they could speak.

'I don't know what it is I am doing,' she says. 'I cannot
explain how it works. I just put my hands on the animal and
let them go where they want upon the body. I am not guiding
them myself. I am channelling a healing energy which comes
from somewhere else. I don't know where.'

But she also insists: 'I do not believe there are gifted people who have the power of healing. I think this is an energy that we can all tap into. We might not be aware of it. But I strongly believe that healing is an integral part of us all.'

Healing cures a herd of cows

Harry Edwards, the doyen of British spiritual healers, was once called upon to heal a herd of cows. The farmer visited the healer and said the vet had diagnosed them all as suffering from chronic streptococci mastitis. This serious condition causes the cows' udders to become hard and sore, and might mean they would never be suitable again for milk production, in which case they would have to be destroyed. The healer promised to start absent healing immediately and instructed the farmer to return to the herd and begin gently massaging their udders while holding the thought in his mind that the mastitis would go.

'The farmer did this,' Edwards wrote, 'and, while it may be hard for a sceptic to believe, the morning after he found all the udders soft and by the end of the day all symptoms of hardness and soreness had disappeared.' Not only that, but their milk production returned to normal a day later. This was so unlikely that when the astonished vet examined them he exclaimed, 'What is the matter with me; have I been dreaming?'

Another of Edwards' animal patients was a talking budgerigar named Tony with an extensive vocabulary. He became ill, lost his feathers and moped. His distressed owner, who lived in Southampton, not only wrote for absent healing but taught the bird to say, 'Harry Edwards heal me'! It worked and Tony soon had even brighter plumage than before. Whenever he showed signs of sickness his owner always sought Edwards' help and the budgerigar proved to be very responsive to healing, living to a ripe old age.

Edwards' favourite animal healing story concerned an Alsatian which was brought to his Surrey sanctuary in a van. It was too sick to be taken out, so Edwards climbed into the van to give healing.

'The dog was lying on blankets, and as I looked at it, it

seemed very near to death. The body was wasted and very thin, the hind part of the body and legs were paralysed, and the dog's eyes were sunken and glazed over.'

Edwards sat down by the dog for a while, holding its head in his hands as he sought healing help for it. There seemed to be no response and in the end Edwards laid the dog's head gently down and went into the house with its owners to have a cup of tea. He told them he thought the dog was dying.

When they were about to leave, Edwards suggested taking one more look at the Alsatian:

> When the rear van doors were opened our astonishment was great, for there stood the dog, standing up on his four legs and wagging his tail! He joyously came towards us, but did not go to his master or mistress, coming straight to me, to be fondled as if he knew quite well that he had to express his gratitude. We gave the dog some milk and food which pleased my visitors for he had not been able to take any nourishment for some time.

Animal healing in the laboratory

Such stories may not convince sceptics, who will dismiss them as anecdotal – even though many of the cures or improvements have been verified by vets. But let us not forget that animal healing has been demonstrated under laboratory conditions. Some of the very earliest double-blind experiments with healers used mice as the 'patients'. These were made to suffer in some way – either by wounding or being injected with disease – and then a healer would be directed to give healing to one group but not another. These tests, as discussed in Chapter Five, produced statistically significant results. And the reason researchers used mice, or barley seeds, or other living organisms, instead of human patients, was to overcome the criticism that the healing was produced by the subconscious. In other words, there could be no suggestion that the results were produced by a placebo effect.

Can dolphins heal, too?

Finally, before we leave the fascinating subject of animals and healing, we have to consider the possibility – however unlikely – that some animals also possess healing powers. Dolphins, in particular, are reputed to be therapeutic swimming partners for those humans fortunate enough to be able to frolic in the water with them. Cosima Somerset, who suffered from depression, told *Daily Telegraph* readers in January 1998 of her visit to the Red Sea to swim with Ollen, a female dolphin who was always pleased to meet new playmates.

'The warm welcome from Ollen touched me beyond words, as did her gentleness with me, as if she sensed my need for tenderness.'

She was told by her escort, Edgar, an actor who believes dolphins are spiritual guides, that he had seen Ollen deliberately nudge people and he believed these movements were part of a healing process. For example, she had nudged a woman with multiple sclerosis, Cosima Somerset reported, 'in a way that caused a shift to take place which had subsequently helped her condition'. As for herself, she found that swimming with Ollen had altered her perspective. On her return home she found that 'something had changed inside me'. She concluded with these words: 'A month later, I feel that this is permanent; it has not left me. Thank you Ollen for your exceptional gift.'

Cosima Somerset is not alone in believing that dolphins are very special creatures, though the improvements which many people report from their encounters with them could be explained by the 'feel-good' factor – the placebo effect. But when humans claiming special powers bring about miraculous healings in animals, it seems we need to look further afield for a satisfactory explanation.

11

A HEALING FORCE

Lim Kyongtaek clambered over the huge mound of rubble which had once been the Sampoong Department Store in the centre of Seoul, South Korea. Around him, rescuers tore at the stones with their hands while others used mechanical diggers to gently lift tons of debris. One by one, they discovered a few lucky survivors and the crushed bodies of over 200 shoppers who had died when the building collapsed without warning in June 1995.

It was now nine days after that tragic event and the rescuers held out little hope of finding anyone else alive. Every so often they would stop so that sensitive sound detectors could listen for faint cries. They heard nothing. But some of the grieving families still hoped for a miracle, and so they called on the elderly Lim Kyongtaek, an expert in the ancient art of qi (pronounced 'chee') – also known as ki and chi – to visit the scene to see if his special powers would be more successful than conventional science in locating survivors. As a qi master, he would be able to sense the presence of qi in anyone who was still alive beneath the rubble. (Qi is the term used in traditional Chinese medicine for the life force or energy – also our vital breath.)

Lim, incidentally, is more than a man with unusual powers. He is also a respected professor of political science at Mokpo University.

Eventually, after checking the collapsed building, he pin-pointed a place where he was certain there was a survivor. What was more, he said it was a young, healthy male, possibly a sportsman, who was emitting qi. Rescuers were sceptical, since the area Lim indicated was at the very centre of the building, the very last place they would expect to find survivors. But they made a search and found . . . nothing. The puzzled professor left the site shaking his head and remarking that it was strange.

This story, I'm delighted to say, has a happy ending. Some twelve hours later, a young Korean man, Choi Myong-suk, *was* dug out at the spot. Lim had been right, after all.

The difference between the physical detection methods used by the rescuers and Lim's approach was that the former were looking for signs of a living *body*, such as heat or sound, whereas Lim was hoping to sense a body's *life force*. Only a human receptor can do that.

'Bio-energy' taught thousands of years ago

What is known as qi, ki or chi in the Far East has no direct Western equivalent but is akin to 'bio-energy' or electromagnetic energy. Such beliefs, it is claimed, derive from Qigong – a discipline which has been described as the mother of traditional Chinese medicine and is said to be thousands of years old. But it was only known to an elite until the 1980s, apparently, when the veil of secrecy was lifted and the results of various research programmes began to be published. Now, Qigong is enjoying growing popularity, which is hardly surprising since it promises those who follow its philosophy and practices that it will increase their energy level, enhance sexual performance, help them lose weight, relieve fatigue and pain, delay the ageing process and reverse paralysis.

This is not the place to examine such claims in detail, but the book *Qigong: miracle healing from China* by Dr Charles T. McGee and San Francisco-based Qigong Master Effie Poy Yew Chow, provides a wealth of healing case studies attributed to Chow's own techniques, which are remarkably similar to the results achieved by spiritual healing in the West.

For example, there is the story of an eight-year-old boy, Eric, who was born with cerebral palsy. His left hand and foot were deformed, he had poor co-ordination and other problems. In particular, the Achilles tendon in his left leg was short, preventing normal ankle movements and causing him to walk permanently on tiptoe. Dr Effie Chow met him when she was invited by a home nurses association to run a seminar on energy and touch healing for seventy-five health professionals. Eric was nominated by his therapists to be a test patient. She asked him what he most wanted to do and he told her it was to ride a skateboard and kick a football. As far as most of those present were concerned, these were impossible dreams. But Dr Chow started with his left hand, which was flexed in a permanently contracted position, placing it in hers and stroking it gently whilst talking to the child.

'Actually,' writes Dr McGee, 'she was using Qigong manoeuvres to flood Eric's tissues with an unseen force or energy, the mysterious thing known as 'qi'. Within only twenty minutes, the impossible began to occur.' Five minutes later, all five fingers could be fully extended and the hand looked normal. He was even able to pick up a large coin with his thumb and forefinger – something he had never done in his life. The audience were so impressed they clapped with joy. And when she performed another miracle with his left foot, enabling him to place it firmly on the ground, Eric's parents openly cried tears of joy. That weekend, he was able to ride a skateboard and kick a football. His two ambitions were fulfilled.

Our internal energy system

There is a growing realisation that healing may draw upon qi – or whatever else we choose to call our mysterious, internal energy system, in which invisible chakras, meridians and other rather strange-sounding parts of our ethereal anatomy are linked. Acupuncture and many alternative therapies lean heavily on such concepts. The First World Conference for

Academic Exchange of Medical Qigong, held in Beijing in 1988, was attended by 600 delegates who heard 137 papers presenting hard data and the results of clinical trials which showed how beneficial the practice of Qigong can be, usually as a self-healing technique but also when received passively from someone who can emit qi energy.

According to Dr McGee:

> The qi system is as distinct as the respiratory and nervous systems. If qi patterns are disrupted by emotional distress, environmental exposures, or any number of factors, a person becomes susceptible to disease. When this disruption of energy is rebalanced, health is restored. In this integrated approach, a person's body, mind and spirit are one, interacting with people, the immediate environment and the Universe.

Our many meridians or channels of energy include twelve major bilateral ones and two other singular ones which go up and down the midline of the body, Dr McGee explains. Along these meridians are over 600 energy points which, when stimulated or sedated in different ways, affect our energy systems. In addition, there are hundreds more which are not on meridians. This has been known for more than 2000 years.

Indeed, the existence of some inner force is even depicted in religious paintings, in which Jesus and the Christian saints are shown with an aura around their heads, and Buddha is shown surrounded by a golden glow. Though many regard this as merely symbolic, others insist that it depicts a very real phenomenon, that we all have auras – akin to an electrical glow – and that the auras of spiritual people are particularly bright and beautiful. But you have to be psychic to see them. Those who can do so claim the aura's shape, colour and brightness tell them much about an individual's mood or state of health.

There have been many attempts to develop a means by which we could all view people's auras. One of the first was by Dr J. Walter Kilner, a British physician, who was in charge of electrotherapy at London's St Thomas's Hospital over one hundred years ago. His book *The Human Atmosphere* was the first scientific study of the phenomenon and it described his experiments with dicyanin, a coal tar derivative, as a filter through which the aura could be viewed.

Taking photographs of our electrical bodies

Some believe a Russian discovery, called Kirlian photography, also provides physical evidence of the human energy system. In fact, something similar had been around for a long time and was known as corona discharge photography. Kirlian photographs show glowing coronas, around the fingertips or a complete hand, which seem to change with mood or other emotions. Kirlian-type devices expose the human body, or an object, to 25,000 volts at very low amperage from a Tesla transformer.

One of those who experimented with high-frequncy Kirlian photography was the late Dr Thelma Moss who carried out tests at the University of California, Los Angeles. As well as standard Kirlian photographic prints, Dr Moss even captured the startling effect in colour on videotape. When one of her experimental subjects placed the side of his face against the photographic plate, it produced a star-studded effect. These bright lights are said to have been located exactly where the face's energy points were drawn in Chinese records over 2000 years ago. In another of her videotaped experiments, a man with an injured left wrist placed both hands on the Kirlian device, which depicted very small halos around the fingers of his left hand and very large ones around those of his right hand. Acupuncture needles were then inserted into energy points and, over a twenty-second period, the small halos grew in size while the right-hand ones diminished, until all ten finger patterns were of equal size and appearance. The balance of his energy, it seemed, had been restored to normal.

What has this to do with healing?

The answer could be that it holds the key to the mechanics of health. Dr Moss's work included experiments to measure changes in the energy patterns of healers before, during and after a healing session. The pictures appear to show a building up of energy in the hands and then a transfer of some of this force to the patient. This is precisely what many healers visualise as they heal their patients. After the treatment, the glow in the healer's hands has diminished, whereas the patient's energy field seems to have grown.

That, at least, was Dr Moss's interpretation of what she was recording, but not everyone would agree with it. American biochemist Glen Rein, for example, conducted Kirlian research work at Queen Charlotte's Hospital in London, in which tissue samples from women with breast cancer were compared with samples from healthy women. Rein found that the light intensity emitted from the tissues of the women with cancer was *greater* and larger than that from the healthy women. However, in the late 1970s, biophysicist Leonard W. Konikiewicz and his Polyclinic Medical Centre colleagues in Harrisburg, Pennsylvania, reported that negative feelings, including apprehension and animosity, weakened the intensity of the inner corona given off by the hands. Joy and sexual excitement, however, make the corona stronger.

So, whilst no one doubts that Kirlian photography is a real phenomenon, we have to be careful not to jump to too many conclusions about it at this stage. That has not prevented a number of commercially minded people from leaping on the bandwagon and offering Kirlian readings. I gave it a try many years ago when I visited a stand at the Mind, Body, Spirit Exhibition in London. Following instructions, I placed my hands on the photographic plate and, once it was developed, took my intriguing, black-and-white life-energy snapshot to one of the many readers waiting to give me an interpretation. What she told me sounded much like what I would have heard from a crystal-ball gazer or a tarot card reader. Half an hour later I repeated the exercise, taking my new Kirlian handprints to a different reader. The coronas were not the same as the first and his interpretation of my physical state of health was also different.

Of course, said the stand's owner, when I challenged him. I'd spent half an hour walking around the exhibition before having the second Kirlian session, so I was tireder and that was reflected in the results. The second set of coronas would have been smaller than the first, he suggested . . . and he was right. But he failed to convince me that those employed on his stand to interpret the Kirlian effect were qualified to do so. After all, on what were they basing their knowledge? During a visit to the same exhibition in 1997, incidentally, Kirlian photography was in even greater demand than before but this time with a twist. They were combining a straightforward photographic portrait picture of each customer with a Kirlian fingerprint, then superimposing one over the other, producing something that looked remarkably like an aura around the subject's head. This time, I kept my money firmly in my wallet.

Sceptics argue that Kirlian photography is recording nothing more spiritual than perspiration or other substances on the skin's surface, and have demonstrated that the effects produced can be made to vary enormously just by varying the amount of pressure used, or changing other factors.

Machine can trace human energy flow

Having said that, it is possible that Kirlian photography might eventually teach us something about our life force, and researchers are continuing to use it in their studies in a variety of ways. Meanwhile, scientists are looking at other ways of detecting and recording the force of qi. For example, Japanese researcher Hiroshi Motoyama has developed a machine called the AMI, an acronym for 'apparatus for meridian identification', that has successfully located and measured energy flowing through the meridians. It has achieved this by recording the flow of ions through 'ionic stream beds' just beneath the skin's surface. The patterns of flowing ions detected by the AMI correspond with those of the acupuncture meridians recognised for thousands of years. But they are *not* our vital energy, or qi, itself. Motoyama explains that it is a parallel electromagnetic effect and an indicator of the flow of qi. The same researcher is also said to have produced the first objective evidence for the existence of chakras by positioning copper electrodes close to the body in front of the areas where chakras are traditionally believed to be situated.

Scientists at the Massachusetts Institute of Technology, at the State University of New York, and other research centres are also studying the body's electromagnetic field to find out, in the words of MITT researcher David Cohen, 'what can be seen through the new window'. It is even reported by some investigators that our meridians emit light which can actually be seen with infra-red photography and that an isotope, when injected into an energy point, can be tracked as it travels up or down a meridian channel exactly as shown in ancient qi charts.

The Chinese are not alone, of course, in believing that we are somehow animated by an unseen force of bio-energy, as Bill Schul points out in *Psychic Frontiers of Medicine*: 'In India they refer to this force as prana, the one energy in which everything is enveloped. Mesmer called it animal magnetism. Reichenbach referred to it as odic force. Keely named it motor force. Blondlot called it N rays. The radiothesists refer to it as etheric force. Soviet scientists call it psychotronic energy.'

Discoverer of 'orgone' had his books burnt

Missing from that list, curiously, is Dr Wilhelm Reich, one of Sigmund Freud's most talented and original pupils, whose ideas – particularly on sex – infuriated and outraged his more puritanical colleagues. Dr Reich believed he had discovered a new form of fundamental energy and that this primordial or cosmic orgone energy – orgone for short – was a continuum of the energy that surrounds us. Distinct from electromagnetism, and travelling at the speed of light in waves, he believed it penetrated everything to some degree.

Having discovered orgone, Dr Reich set about harnessing it by building an 'accumulator' made of wood and metal, from which a tube 'shot' the power outside to be used for healing purposes. Later, he built a bigger accumulator so that the patient could sit inside during treatment. It may sound like the work of a crank, but an English medical man, Dr Aubrey T. Westlake, is reported to have used a Reich 'shooter' device to cure pain and speed up the healing of wounds and burns. Dr Andrew Stanway, in his book *Alternative Medicine – a guide to natural therapies*, tells us that a doctor friend of his was treated by Dr Westlake's orgone 'shooter' for synovitis of the knee. After an initial sensation of coolness, he experienced a definite improvement within half an hour, 'after which the pain did not return'.

Unfortunately, during an experiment in 1950, Dr Reich tried to show that orgone could counteract the dangers of radiation. There was an unexpected reaction between the orgone and radium, and all his institute's mice died and many of his colleagues suffered from radiation sickness. This only added to his problems, for he had long been hounded by the authorities who seemed eager to put a stop to his work.

In 1954 an injunction was served on him and his foundation, preventing the distribution of the devices '. . . all accumulators to be disassembled, all printed matter regarding these and orgone energy to be destroyed *on the grounds that orgone energy does not exist.*' Reich was arrested and jailed, dying of a heart attack two years later, at the age of seventy, while still in prison. Had he really discovered a new force? It is difficult to tell since all his research papers were incinerated by the authorities after his arrest. Conspiracy theorists, however, suggest that the United States government's determination to destroy everything associated with orgone research points to Dr Reich having made a discovery of major importance which it felt the public – or maybe medical or pharmacological interests – could not handle.

Beings of energy

Although all these cultures and scientific discoveries seem to be saying the same thing – that we are beings of energy – it is becoming more and more difficult for laymen to understand such claims, or their importance, without a knowledge of science. My own interpretation is that we are, indeed, more than flesh and blood. Ultimately, we are souls, but with intermediary bodies which are necessary to allow our souls to manifest in a physical realm. Our bodies also generate electrical, electromagnetic or life force energy in a complex matrix which, as well as having significance in healing, could be a vital means of communication and coherence between our physical, astral, spirit, etheric or soul bodies – call them what you will. Furthermore, this life force may be a means of communication with others, as we will see in Chapter Fourteen.

Morphic resonance

Coping with such ideas is not easy. We are all used to equating reality with the world of physical matter, and most of us dismiss anything we cannot experience with our five senses. But that leaves a lot of questions unanswered. Biologist Dr Rupert Sheldrake, however, has come up with a theory which makes sense of many of the phenomena we have been discussing, as well as explaining other mysteries of nature. Though it has yet to win widespread scientific approval, his 'morphic resonance' hypothesis seems to have a fair measure of popular support.

He explains that he used to share the commonly held belief that living organisms were nothing more than complex machines governed only by the known laws of physics and chemistry. But over a period of several years he realised that this assumption was difficult to justify. He now believes that natural systems, or morphic units, at all levels of complexity – atoms, molecules, crystals, cells, tissues, organs, organisms, and societies of organisms – are animated, organised, and co-ordinated by morphic fields, which contain an inherent memory. Natural systems inherit this collective memory from all previous things of their kind by a process called morphic resonance, resulting in patterns of development and behaviour which become increasingly habitual through repetition. Sheldrake suggests that there is a continuous spectrum of morphic fields, including morphogenetic fields, behavioural fields, mental fields, and social and cultural fields.

His ideas are far too complex to examine here in detail, but they provide us with a framework within which healing, telepathy and a range of other so-called paranormal phenomena make sense.

Salamander knows its leg from its tail

Among those doing work on healing and the life force is Dr Robert Becker, an orthopaedic surgeon and former professor of Upstate Medical Centre, Syracuse, NY. He and his colleagues have shown that a number of techniques, such as acupuncture, diet and healing touch, boost the body's internal electrical currents and result in a strengthening of the body's healing mechanism, including the immune, endocrine and nervous systems. In his book, *Cross Currents* (1990), Dr Becker reports on the laboratory evidence which is shedding light on how healing touch may work.

Dr Becker writes that he has 'seen remarkable results obtained in a number of life-threatening circumstances,' adding:

> Since we know that the body uses electrical control systems to regulate many basic functions and that the flow of these electrical currents produces externally measurable magnetic fields, it does not require a great leap of faith to postulate that the healer's gift is an ability to use his or her own electromagnetic energy fields that interact with those of the patient. The interaction could be one of those that 'restores' balance in the internal forces or that reinforces the electrical

systems so that the body returns toward a normal condition.

In fact, this energetic body, this life force matrix, may serve as a blueprint which literally shapes our lives. Like Sheldrake, Dr Becker calls it a 'morphogenic field', and believes it contains a unique intelligence that controls the growth, development and health of cells and tissues. His evidence for this came during a series of remarkable experiments on salamanders, which are well known for their ability to regrow in perfect detail a new tail. In fact, they can regrow most parts of their bodies if damaged, including a leg, an eye, an ear, half a heart, as much as one-third of a brain, and most of their digestive tract.

As part of their life force investigations, Dr Becker and other researchers at State University New York, severed the tail and leg of a salamander. Sure enough, as expected, the animal began to grow replacements at the point of amputation. Then, in a departure from similar research in the past, Dr Becker took some of the cells that were developing into a new tail and placed them on the stump of the amputated leg. It was assumed that the DNA in these cells was pre-programmed and these cells would continue to grow into a tail. But they didn't. The new tail cells grew into a leg which was complete in every detail. He reversed the process by placing newly growing leg cells on the stump of the tail. They became a new tail.

Dr Becker went on to show that new cells, taken from any amputation site on the salamander's body and placed elsewhere at a new site, whether heart, brain, or intestine, will become that new part of the body. But why? What changes the orders to the DNA? One possibility was that this change occurred at the amputation site, through local nerves. But the researchers demonstrated that the nerves were completely 'silent', transmitting neither impulses nor information.

After another series of experiments, according to Deborah Cowens in *A Gift for Healing*:

Becker discovered that there was indeed a 'larger intelligence' that existed as an electrical field, surrounding and infusing the salamander's body. Becker proved that this larger electrical body, a 'morphogenic field', actually organises and orders the DNA to produce whatever the body needs at a particular site. His work with salamanders proved that the information is passed from this morphogenic field to the animal's body, which triggers the appropriate DNA response and in turn produces the appropriate organ. The morphogenic field also plays a role in the healing powers of acupuncture and healing touch. The field directs more life energy to specific parts of the body that need healing. Becker demonstrated that whenever a person is cut, injured, or suffers from an illness, the body increases the flow of direct-current electricity, which provides the essential energy for healing, to the injured or diseased site.

Subtle energies and biofields

British zoologist and healer Dr Toni Bunnell, whose research work was discussed in Chapter Five, also favours an electro-magnetic explanation for healing results. She points out that researcher A. Seto published a paper titled 'Detection of extraordinarily large bio-magnetic field strength from human during external Qi emission' in the *International Journal of Acupuncture and Electro-therapeutics* (Vol 17, 1992). This demonstrated that during healing a force 1000 times greater than that of normal human bio-magnetism can be produced. Where does it come from?

She turns for an answer to another well-documented phe-nomenon related to healing. Studies in which the healer and the patient had their brainwaves monitored have revealed that the healer, in preparing to give healing, produces alpha brain waves (which range between 7 and 12 Hz) causing deep relaxation. Furthermore, research has shown that during the treatment the healer's alpha brainwaves synchronise with those of the patient so that both are resonating on the same frequency. 'In other words.' Dr Bunnell told me, 'channelling energy through the healer and to the healee involves both being in the alpha state.'

Dr Bunnell describes this as 'sympathetic resonance' and she goes on to say that such brainwaves, in the alpha state, 'will resonate at the vibrational frequency of the Earth's electromagnetic frequency, producing constructive interference which amplifies the vibration'. In other words, they are drawing on an infinite energy source – the Earth's – to boost the patient's energy system. 'If, for some reason, the cells begin to oscillate at a less than optimal frequency due to localised injury, emotional trauma, magnetic field deficiency or some other cause,' says Dr Bunnell, 'then hands-on healing may be exerting its effect by jump-starting the system to redirect or divert energy flow.'

Such studies are being grouped together and viewed as the new science of neuromagnetics. But those involved in such work tell us that this greater understanding of man as an electric animal has important implications which have hitherto been ignored. Dr Bunnell, for example, cautions healers not to treat patients if they, themselves, feel unwell, depressed or tired. Transferring energy in that condition can be harmful.

Meanwhile, Robert Becker has produced a sequel to his book *The Body Electric*, Called *Cross Currents*, its subtitle warns of 'the perils of electropollution' but also 'the promise of electromedicine'. In it he voices his concern about the impact which the worldwide electric power grid might be having on us.

Those working in the field of biomagnetism or neuromagnetics are hoping to find a way to measure the human life force in the same way that units of electricity are measured. Indeed, one suggestion is that we call this force, which seems to act as a bridge between spirit and matter, para-electricity. And that each unit of para-electricity be called a 'Worrall' after the famous healers Ambrose and Olga Worrall.

Another name that has been suggested for this vital energy is 'biofield'. Richard Pavek, of the Biofield Research Institute in Sausalito, California, advocates this term because, in his view, it captures the essential meanings of *life field*, *life force* and *life energy*. There is even a new term used by most researchers to describe the subject they are investigating as a whole. It is 'subtle energies'.

At the moment, these energies may be too subtle for the public to comprehend, but they promise, in time, to change the whole way we look at the workings of our minds and bodies . . . and perhaps provide an explanation for how healing takes place.

12

THE EVIDENCE FOR HEALING

With so many instances of healing having been reported in all cultures over many centuries, it is surely a little surprising that no one has yet come up with incontrovertible proof. Taken as a whole – as Dr Daniel Benor has shown in his superb survey of spiritual healing research – there really is a wealth of evidence from reputable sources which ought to put the matter beyond doubt. But to absorb that evidence one has to read a mountain of medical and scientific literature. What would be more impressive would be a wide-ranging experiment, with total medical support, in which a large number of patients were examined before and after healing, and subsequently over a long period. But who would pay for it? Certainly not the pharmaceutical companies who usually fund medical research. Why would they spend their fortunes on studying a form of therapy which, if found to be effective, could damage their sales? But probably the biggest obstacle to acceptance of the evidence, so far, has been the lack of an all-embracing theory to explain healing. Until such a theory appears, individuals will have to make their own decisions as to whether they should consult healers.

Healing for England

As the England football team plotted their strategy in the

run-up to the 1998 World Cup, rumours began to circulate that they had a secret weapon which would help them win the coveted trophy. Was this just part of the psychological warfare that goes on in competitive sports, or was there a grain of truth in it? The answer was that it *was* true. What's more, England's footballer-turned-coach Glenn Hoddle decided to spill the beans in April 1998, just two months before England's first game in France against Tunisia. And the secret, to many people's astonishment, was that the England squad were using a healer, Eileen Drewery, to help them overcome injury problems.

Physical fitness is essential for professional sportspeople, and yet, by their very nature, their activities – particularly in contact sports – frequently result in injuries which put them out of action, sometimes for long periods. Teams of physio-therapists, masseurs and doctors are employed by football teams to get their high-priced players back on the pitch as fast as possible. But sometimes their combined talents are not enough.

English soccer fans were already aware of Hoddle's inter-est in healing. It had come to light six months earlier when his marriage of eighteen years ended and he took refuge in the Berkshire home of Eileen Drewery, a grandmother. This led to some wild speculation about the relationship between the 56-year-old healer and the 39-year-old father of three, who is a devout Christian. But it soon emerged that he had known her since he was a Tottenham teenager dating her daughter, Michelle. The Drewerys then ran a pub, and sev-enteen-year-old Hoddle sat in their kitchen, sipping tea while receiving healing for a hamstring injury. Eileen told him it would be fine the next day, and as predicted it was free of pain when he turned up for a training session. Since then, Drewery, whose husband is now a bricklayer, has helped heal him of many football injuries as well as giving him spiritual guidance. And it is reported that during his playing days, she would scour the newspapers for reports of his overseas games and send him distant healing if he was injured.

What came as a surprise to English soccer fans, however, was to learn that three-quarters of the 32-strong English squad have also been treated by Drewery for a year and a half. They have done so of their own volition, having seen the benefits Hoddle and other colleagues have derived from healing.

'If you ridicule it, you've got a closed mind,' Hoddle told the press. 'I've seen plenty of people go to see Drewery cynically and it changed their lives. From my Swindon days, she's saved players' careers.'

One of those who was happy to testify to her healing powers was Arsenal captain and England striker Ian Wright. 'I've been going to Eileen for eight or nine months now. She's helped me to be positive. She means a lot to me. I feel very close to her. She's blessed. Some people can take it on board, some will say it's rubbish. I've been God-fearing, involved with spiritual stuff, all my life. I've been seeing faith-healers for years, even in my time at Crystal Palace.'

The once-volatile Wright has been dogged by injuries but his encounters with Drewery seem to have helped him cope with the mental frustrations as well as the physical damage.

It was a change of outlook which the *Daily Mail*'s chief football writer, Graham Hunter, noticed:

Out for almost three months with a succession of injuries, Wright is calm, positive and overwhelmingly at ease with himself despite what he stands to miss out on. He believes he owes what recovery he has made and his state of mind to Eileen Drewery and, despite an intense dislike of being derided, he is willing to say as much . . .

He is articulate and deeply enthusiastic about his life and for a man who stands to lose so much through his injuries – a World Cup place and playing in the FA Cup Final at 34 – he is sanguine, not to say positive, about the experience. Something is happening when Drewery is laying her hands on our boys.

Among other top soccer players who are said to have benefited from Drewery's healing are Paul Gascoigne, Darren Anderton – who was nicknamed 'sicknote' after a persistent string of injuries interrupted his burgeoning career – and Micky Hazard.

Eileen Drewery is not the only healer influencing the fortunes of football clubs. In fact, the widespread use of healers is 'the hidden secret of football', according to Jim White, who came to that conclusion while writing a book about Manchester United. He learned that Bryan Robson, the former United and England captain, referred injured players to a healer.

In the end, no amount of healing could keep England in the World Cup, and they were knocked out by Argentina in a penalty shoot-out, after a thrilling and nerve-racking game.

Turned to healer after two operations

Another player who has been helped by healing is Craig Flemming, who was a formidable midfield player for First Division Oldham Athletic Football Club, which had battled its way to an FA Cup semi-final with Manchester United at Wembley in April 1994. Craig's skills were attracting a lot of attention from other clubs, but then he began to be troubled by pain in his leg and hip. Eventually, he underwent two operations to relieve the condition but the improvement fell short of a cure. Craig had heard of healer Lorraine Ham and decided to put himself in her hands. He felt a pins-and-needles sensation as she held her hands above his body, but there were no obvious signs of a cure at the end of this treatment. However, when he attended his next training session the following Monday, and tried various exercises which had caused him pain, there was no problem. 'I let my leg go all the way down and brought it back up again and there was no pain at all. So then I just went on doing these exercises all day. I was a bit flabbergasted by it.'

A similar hip problem affected England rugby international Ben Clarke who turned to healing after extensive and expensive conventional treatments failed to stop it recurring.

He was treated by Malcolm Bessant, (whose healing of an Alsatian was discussed in Chapter Ten). During the healing, Clarke reported feeling some warmth and a pulse around where Bessant was working. However, Bessant worked not on his hip but on his ankle, saying he believed that was where the problem originated. Clarke shared that view. Initially sceptical, the England player became a believer after having three half-hour sessions with Bessant. 'The treatment' Clarke said, 'has achieved a remarkable improvement. I'm absolutely delighted. I wasn't sure about it before. I was very, very sceptical, but I'm certainly convinced of it now.'

Healing helped him become world champion

Another champion sportsman whose name we can add to healing's long list of satisfied customers is English speedway rider Gary Havelock. It can be a dangerous pursuit, as he found out to his cost whilst racing in Europe. A Polish rider lost control, crashing into the back of Havelock's bike and slamming him into the safety fence. Havelock flew over the handlebars and somersaulted down the track, suffering severe bruising and deep gashes to his shoulder. An X-ray at the hospital confirmed he had also broken his right hand and the Polish doctor told him he must take six weeks off racing to allow the bones to knit together.

This was devastating news for Havelock who had to compete in the Commonwealth Final at Kings Lynn, England, in nine days' time, if he was to qualify for a chance in the world championship. So he turned to Lorraine Ham for healing help. When she held her hands over his, he recalls, it was as if someone was holding a blow-torch or heat-lamp close to him. But when she touched his hand 'her fingers were icy cold'. Havelock's hand began to feel better immediately, and the improvement continued rapidly over the next few days.

'When it came to race day, it wasn't 100 per cent, but it was certainly a lot better than it would have been without the treatment,' he explains. 'To do that nine days after breaking some bones in my hand was quite amazing.' He came third at the meeting, which was an impressive performance in the circumstances and, better still, he went on to become the 1992 World Speedway Champion.

Knee cure helped him run into record books

Finally, there is the story of the sensational New Zealand runner John Walker who shattered the world record for the mile in 1974. In August that year, spectators at Gothenburg, Sweden, saw him shave 1.6 seconds off the old world record by running a mile in an amazing 3 minutes 49.4 seconds. But what none of them knew was that two months earlier, Walker had doubted that he would be fit enough to run. In fact, he had so much pain in his knee that he had trouble getting out of bed. Then, turning on the radio in Auckland, his home town, the 23-year-old runner heard a visiting English clairvoyant and healer, Doris Collins, being interviewed on the local Talkback Show by its host Gordon Dryden. The psychic, whose famous clients have included Peter Sellers, explained that she was on a tour demonstrating her powers.

Walker made his way to the studio because he wanted to meet her. He had told few people about the knee problem, which had troubled him for two years. After hard training a chronic pain would develop, the knee would swell and he found it difficult to straighten the leg. He had tried various treatments but it had failed to respond. Collins referred to the knee the moment she met him . . . and set about trying to put it right.

'Mrs Collins put her hands on my spine and on my knees,' he told a newspaper after his sensational record-breaking run. 'I felt vibrations coming through her fingertips! It was uncanny. Incredible. Then, after about five minutes, she asked me to stand up and there was no more pain! The next Saturday, I ran 400 metres fifteen times. If my knee was going to hurt, it would have hurt then. The next day I ran a 17-miler. No trouble!'

And so, when he flew to Sweden in August, he did so confident in the knowledge that he could run better than ever before. And that's what he did, running straight into the record books.

I mention these cases for two reasons. First, sports stars are usually regarded as down-to-earth individuals who take their health and fitness seriously. Second, they usually have the best medical advice and facilities at their disposal in order to shrug off their injuries as quickly as possible. The very fact that these people turn to healers may be seen as an act of desperation on their part, but the results speak for themselves.

Before we speculate any further on what healing is and how it works, let us remind ourselves of some of the methods that are available, the difficulties that face researchers in carrying out experiments, the problems we have in assessing their results, and finally the impressive evidence that has been collected in the past and continues to be recorded with even greater regularity from those who have been helped by healing.

Laying-on-of-hands

Two of the most remarkable American healers, who had each earned a reputation for their extraordinary powers before they married, were Ambrose and Olga Worrall. One of Ambrose's best-documented cases concerned a nine-year-old girl who was brought to him in 1965 with just a few months to live. Laboratory tests confirmed she had Von Hecklinghausen's disease, which causes nodules, and it was spreading rapidly through her body. Ambrose treated the girl daily for three weeks, during which time the soft nodules gradually disappeared and the hard ones began to recede. The progress continued at the end of the treatment and four years later her father wrote to confirm that his daughter was in perfect health and 'all symptoms of the terrible disease were gone.'

Another young girl who was treated by Ambrose was a medical doctor's daughter, who was suffering from a bone disease. X-rays had confirmed her condition and an operation was imperative. Describing what happened when he first treated the child, Ambrose wrote: 'I placed my left hand under her knee and my right hand on her knee cap. I felt the healing current strongly, and in a few minutes I knew the bone was healed. I reported my findings to Dr G, who thought it would be wise to have further X-rays taken because he did not want to delay the operation if it were needed.' The X-rays showed no evidence of the disease, and two years later the child was in excellent health and enjoying skiing and swimming.

Olga Worrall, who outlived her husband but has also now passed away, gave public demonstrations of her healing powers, as well as seeing patients privately and co-operating with scientific tests in laboratories. A friend of Dr Thelma Moss (whose research with healers and Kirlian photography was discussed in Chapter Eleven) reported a dramatic case which she witnessed. The session was held at the New Life Clinic in Baltimore where a woman with an ugly red tumour 'as large as a goose egg', on her cheek, came forward for treatment. 'Olga Worrall placed her hand on the lump,' Moss writes:

> When she removed her hands, the tumour was still there, as red and ugly as before. The woman returned to her pew, where she had to pass two ladies who were seated on the aisle. When she asked permission to get by, the two women gasped (as did my friend, who was sitting nearby, watching), because they saw the tumour apparently melt away. By the time the afflicted woman had seated herself, the tumour was gone.

Therapeutic touch

We have already discussed therapeutic touch, which is used by thousands of nurses and other medical staff in a number of countries, thanks to the pioneering work of Dr Dolores Krieger. But it is important to realise that it remains a controversial method of healing, with possibly as many detractors as supporters, and it is helpful to take time to understand the reasons for this.

'Therapeutic touch is not just putting your hands over a painful area,' Dr Krieger has explained, 'nor is it a massage to loosen muscles. You have to be taught to concentrate and direct your healthy energy to get proper results.' Basic to therapeutic touch, she said in 1979, 'is the concept that the human body has an excess energy. The person who administers therapeutic touch engages in an effort to direct his own excess energies for the use of an ill person, who can be thought of as being in less than an optimal energy state.'

Dr Krieger first used it in her nursing work in 1969, having discovered that her patients reported feeling better when she touched them. By the early 1970s she was carrying out laboratory experiments which examined the biochemical effects of her techniques on haemoglobin, partly to answer sceptical criticism. The results, showing an increase in haemoglobin levels, were impressive enough for her to start teaching other nursing professionals how to use therapeutic touch. In fact, they don't actually touch the person – instead they allow their hands to move over the patient's body sensing any areas where energy might be blocked, then clearing it.

The influence of therapeutic touch continued to spread, but in 1984 two psychiatric nurses from Georgia were highly critical of the earlier research on which the credibility of this healing technique was based. Philip E. Clark of the Dwight David Eisenhower Army Centre in Fort Gordon, and Mary Jo Clark, an assistant professor of nursing at the Medical College of Georgia in Augusta, found scientific fault with every published study of therapeutic touch, including Dr Krieger's original haemoglobin experiments. The Clarks suggested that Dr Krieger may have been biased in selecting subjects she knew would respond well psychologically, that she had evaluated them incorrectly, and encouraged patients to practise meditation while the research was being carried out. Meditation, rather than therapeutic touch, for example, may have achieved the rise in haemoglobin levels.

They also drew attention to something strange: in Dr Krieger's final study, there was also an increase in the haemoglobin levels of the *control* group who were not being treated.

It was not as significant, but why did it occur? They concluded that:

> ... the current research base supporting continued
> nursing practice of therapeutic touch is, at best, weak
> ... without a broader research base, it may be
> presumptuous to teach the art or to seriously discuss
> the use of this practice in the treatment of illness. The
> practice of therapeutic touch by nurses will never gain
> professional credibility without clear, objective evidence
> to support it ...

But this complicated story does not end here, for another researcher published her findings in the same year and they happen to answer all these criticisms.

Dr Janet Quinn, Director of the Department of Medical-Surgical Nursing at the University of South Carolina's College of Nursing in Columbia, has a BA in nursing and also uses therapeutic touch. Describing the very first time she learned to use it, she wrote: 'My hands somehow seemed to know what needed to be done and I let them lead me. I felt the energy of the client balance ... My interaction had finally been therapeutic and beneficial. It was a miraculous day, which I shall never forget.'

She began examining the power of touch and eventually conducted research which primarily replicated a study reported in 1981 by Dr Patricia Heidt, and which she carried out in the same coronary wards in New York. Dr Quinn chose twenty-three women and forty-seven men at St Vincent's Medical Centre to take part in the experiment. She decided not to perform the therapeutic touch procedure herself, but used four nurses who were practitioners and three other nurses who were taught to *imitate* the therapeutic touch ritual but, instead of concentrating on unblocking the patients' energy, they were simply told to mentally count backwards.

The patients, of course, did not know whether the nurses who were treating them were really performing therapeutic touch or giving a fake demonstration. After each session, Dr Quinn asked the patients to evaluate their sense of tension and/or anxiety. The study showed conclusively that the patients who had really received therapeutic touch reported a significant reduction in their fears, whereas the control subjects did not. Realising that sceptics might argue that the nurses who were imitating therapeutic touch may have conveyed this in their behaviour, affecting the results, Dr Quinn arranged for all seven nurses to be videotaped while they were giving treatment. A panel of fifteen judges was then asked to study the videos and try to identify which were the genuine healers and which the fake. They could not tell the difference.

Those who practise therapeutic touch can do so, therefore, in the certain knowledge that there is sound scientific evidence to support their techniques, though it will take even more experiments of this kind to silence the sceptics.

Psychic surgery

When American Jane Katra, who holds a doctorate in public health education, went to the Philippines in 1974 to study the so-called psychic surgeons, she arranged with a newspaper that she would write reports of the operations she witnessed. After watching many, and hearing the many stories of trickery, she left as confused as when she arrived, and she could not bring herself to send back any reports. But she has now written about her experiences in *Miracles of the Mind*, a book she has co-authored with physicist and parapsychologist Russell Targ.

Katra visited the Philippines at the time when Americans were being warned not to be fooled by psychic quackery and travel agents were being instructed not to include the words 'psychic surgery' when promoting visits to the islands. Nevertheless, there were several Americans staying at the same hotel who had come to receive psychic surgery. One was a man who told Katra that healer Thelma Zuniga was about to operate on his haemorrhoids. He asked her to video the surgery. 'I want to show my friends and family what they did when I get home!' he explained.

Rather reluctantly, Katra agreed and got in close as the healer's fingers began pressing the man's buttocks. 'Watery, blood-like fluid oozed down his thighs, and in a minute or so some purplish tissue appeared in Thelma's fingers,' she wrote 'It looked like clusters of tiny grapes. She wiped his bottom with a wad of cotton and said, "Okay. Finished." '

Next morning, when she met the man again in the hotel, a rather embarrassed Katra asked, 'So, how are your haemorrhoids today?'

'Honey, they're gone! It's great!'

'Are you sure?' she asked sceptically.

'You bet I'm sure! I've been tucking those darn things in every morning for the past fifteen years, and when I tell you they've gone, believe me, I know what I'm talking about! They're gone!'

Despite the evidence of her own eyes and the man's remarkable testimony, Katra was still not certain what to believe. Then Thelma invited her into the hotel room to watch further operations. Her first patient was a Swiss woman with varicose veins. Katra watched as Thelma began massaging her legs and what looked like blood began to appear:

> Right in the middle of the operation and prayers, a
> dark-suited man followed by two others barged into
> our room, and announced that he was an agent of the
> US government. He acted like a character in a James
> Bond movie as he ponderously declared that he would
> be staying all day to observe the proceedings. I was
> outraged at his rudeness, and felt embarrassed to be of
> the same nationality. He was oblivious to the naked
> Swiss woman's shock and embarrassment, as she
> groped for her clothing and asked in flustered German,
> 'What's going on?'

Thelma was calm and assured the woman that the agent's presence would not affect the efficacy of her healing treatment. As the Swiss woman left, Thelma turned to the US agent, introduced herself and said he was welcome to observe her healing. Then she looked at a ridged bump on his forearm.

'What's this?' she asked, pointing to the purplish bump, which was about an inch long.

'Oh, it's nothing,' he said, clearly flustered.

'May I look at it?' she asked.

'It's really of no consequence,' he protested. 'It's been there for so many years, that I'd forgotten it was even there.'

'Would you like me to get rid of it for you?' Thelma asked.

He was clearly embarrassed at being the centre of attention, but Thelma led him to the bed and indicated that he should lie down. Katra takes up the story:

> I stood at the man's head and watched intently. I observed him as the healer moved her hand back and forth about an inch above the bluish protrusion. She gently swept the air over the lump with the palm of her right hand. Then she held her right palm open above the bump, and kept it there for a while . . .
>
> Thelma began to scratch the lump with her thumbnail. For the first time, I noticed a dark speck, like an elongated pore, on the surface of the bump. Thelma picked at it a bit with her fingernail, and pulled up, seemingly from out of the pore, a thin, elongated piece of tissue . . .

The healer said it was the root of the growth on his arm, and now that it was removed, the lump would recede and be gone within two weeks. Katra met him again two days later when she returned to Thelma's hotel room:

> The US agent was already there. He stood quietly and courteously over to one side of the room, as he observed the day's 'surgeries'. His respectful manner was extremely different from that of his first encounter with Thelma. I was surprised at his transformed demeanour. I asked him, 'How is that growth on your

arm?' He showed me the place where Thelma had scratched a few days before. The ridge was one-third as high as it had been previously, and its colour had changed from purple to pink. 'Oh,' he assured me, in a matter-of-fact tone. 'It's almost gone now. I think it will be entirely gone by the end of the week.'

I wouldn't have believed it was the same man if I hadn't talked to him myself!

Medical support

Most of us are naturally impressed by statistics and experiments, and we tend to seek scientific confirmation of our beliefs wherever possible. This is because they show that improvements in health as a result of such interventions are not isolated cases but are a repeatable and measurable phenomenon. But, of course, the most moving evidence for spiritual healing comes not from laboratory data but from patients' personal testimonies. And such statements have added weight when they are confirmed by doctors who have been directly involved. Over the past two decades spiritual healing has increasingly been embraced by the medical profession, even to the extent of being offered alongside conventional medicine in doctors' surgeries.

The healing reputation of Lorraine Ham, for example, was so impressive that general practitioner Dr Geoffrey Hall of the Bridge Street Surgery in Otley, Yorkshire, invited her to join his busy practice. He knew she had been working with cancer patients at Cookridge Hospital in Leeds and was satisfied that her gift could assist some of the patients who were beyond his help and that of his eight medical colleagues at their centre. Lorraine Ham accepted the invitation in 1990 and the doctors have not been disappointed.

Dr Hall says that the patients Lorraine sees are those whom traditional medicine cannot help. 'When I was a student I was taught all the things that Western medicine can do, and like most doctors I've learned by long and sometimes bitter experience all the things it can't do. Sometimes we reach the limit of Western medical technology, yet we know help is still needed. Those are the kind of patients we are referring to Lorraine.'

The practice partners send most of their patients with long-term chronic physical diseases to Lorraine, and often they have emotional complications. 'Lorraine seems to achieve particularly good results with this group,' says Dr Hall. 'I have been surprised at what she's been able to do. She's been far more successful than I anticipated. Approximately 80 per cent of all people who are referred to her feel they have benefited, and many have been greatly improved by her treatment.'

Dr Michael Dixon, a GP in Cullompton, Devon, also employs a healer in his practice and, like Dr Hall, refers chronically ill patients to the healer – often with startling results.

Dr Michelle Langdon has no need to employ a healer at her medical practice – she does the healing herself after discovering her powers eighteen months ago. 'It doesn't come from me, it comes *through* me,' she explains. 'At first I was worried about patients' reactions. I didn't want them to see me as a crank, but now most of them welcome it. I see it as an extra clinical tool I have, because it works. The advantage is that I am prescribing far fewer anti-inflammatory drugs and pain-killers.'

These UK medical–healing partnerships confirm the view of Dr Daniel Benor, a quiet, bearded New Yorker who trained first as a physician and then studied psychiatry, that 'Britain . . . has always been in the forefront of the modern movement to recover lost healing arts'. In 1987, he moved from the USA to London because he believed 'the healers were much more professional, the doctors more open, and the government itself had given some measure of recognition to non-medical approaches.' Since then, he has become a leading researcher and spokesman for medically qualified individuals who are interested in healing. He is also a leading light in a network of doctor–healer teams across England which provides a forum for those keen to integrate spiritual healing and conventional medicine.

Benor, who now lives in the United States once more, has already published the first instalment of a four-volume reference work on healing, *Healing Research*, the first of its kind and the result of ten years of study. In it he expresses his own views and theories, provides some 1500 references to books and articles on healing, and includes detailed discussion of nearly 150 research projects that offer objective evidence of healing's efficacy. He is convinced, 'emotionally and intellectually', that healing works, adding, 'If spiritual healing were a drug, they'd have put it out there on the market long ago. There's more evidence of its effectiveness than there is of all the other complementary therapies together – from chiropractic or shiatsu to aromatherapy – except perhaps for hypnosis.'

Today, as well as running his private practice in which spiritual healing plays an integral role, Dr Benor lectures on therapeutic touch and spiritual healing to British doctors, medical students, nurses, and other medical professionals – often at the invitation of medical schools or associations. And he has found that 90 per cent of those who attend display a measure of healing ability.

'It will come as news to many in North America that there are now at least three general practice surgeries in England with spiritual healers paid by the government under the National Health Service,' writes Tom Harpur in *The Uncommon Touch*:

> A growing number of British doctors now refer their patients to healers at the healers' treatment rooms. A dozen or so doctors to date have declared they are developing their own innate healing powers. Two hospital pain centres and two hospital cancer centres have healers on the staff of the health team.
>
> Since the mid-1970s, according to Benor, some 1500 healers have had access to British hospitals. There are sixteen different spiritual healing associations, which together form the Confederation of Healing Organisations. The largest of these, the National

Federation of Spiritual Healers, has 5000 healers in its membership. The rest together have about 3000.

Those statistics were put together in 1994, but already they have changed. More up-to-date figures were published in 1998 by the President of the National Federation of Spiritual healers, Craig Brown, who also happens to be both a general practitioner and a healer. In his book, *Optimum Healing*, Dr Brown tells us that there are now some 20,000 healers in Britain, of whom 7500 belong to his organisation, and that they are increasingly to be found in doctors' surgeries and hospitals. His own practice is in West Sussex where he looks after the health of 12,000 patients and where he has employed a spiritual healer for twelve years. Dr Brown's own healing method usually involves gently touching or tapping the body. 'Something really happens,' he says. 'I cannot explain it, but there is a definite shift within the patient.'

Those who believe in spiritual healing are in good company, Dr Brown adds. The Prince of Wales is certainly a believer – and a supporter of many other alternative treatments. Prince Charles spoke in 1997 about Britain reaching a 'defining moment' in healthcare and said it had a 'unique opportunity' to build an integrated health system of complementary medicines alongside the latest in conventional research. He is hoping that all the knowledge, experience and wisdom accumulated in different ways, at different times and in different cultures will be 'effectively deployed to prevent or alleviate human suffering' and is working hard with others to achieve that goal.

Meanwhile, even Prince Charles's polo ponies are reported to receive spiritual healing when the need arises.

13

THE POWER OF LOVE

Perhaps all this talk of invisible energies and forces at work in the healing process just complicates the picture. Could it be that healing, whether through physical contact with the patient or 'transmitted' over a distance, is no more or less than an expression of love?

This poses a problem for those who are looking for scientific confirmation of healing. Love, after all, cannot be measured in a laboratory and is therefore as invisible, intangible and mysterious as healing. But we know love exists. We feel it and we know how powerful it can be. When we are *in* love it affects us deeply; indeed, it can have both an emotional and a physical impact on us. When we are with the person we love, we sometimes feel our love pouring out, as if it were a physical energy. And when we are loved by someone, we sometimes feel bathed in the intense love they feel for us.

There are many forms of love, of course, ranging from materialistic passion for possessions and person-to-person love, to altruistic, unconditional love for others. Perhaps it is the latter which is the channel for healing. If so, those who wish to develop their healing gifts have no need to visualise a flow of energy, or concentrate on chakras and meridians. All that is necessary is to send out loving thoughts to someone else, whether close or far away.

'I believe that this attitude of willingness to be used as an

avenue of help by a primary healing consciousness is what
spiritual masters have called "love", "compassion" and
"charity",' says Jane Katra, co-author of *Miracles of the
Mind*:

> The motivation behind my willingness to practise as a
> spiritual healer is my belief that we are all connected at
> some level: we are one great mind that reveals itself
> through us when we allow it to do so. The practice of
> spiritual healing involves surrender, or the cessation, of
> my own desires and thoughts (selflessness), so that the
> harmonising, balancing life force can flow through me.
> Anyone can decide to do this. I hope more people try it.

Healers are only human

Love may be too simple a formula for many people to accept,
particularly those who prefer to believe that as healers they
are involved with a science, requiring specific knowledge and
the development of special techniques. The evidence, however, suggests otherwise.

I have known many healers over the years, and they are all
remarkably different. They have their faults and foibles.
Some like to drink or smoke or swear. Most enjoy life to the
full. They are, after all, human beings like the rest of us, and
few choose to cloak themselves in an aura of piety. What they
all have in common, however, is compassion for their fellow
human beings. Many healers refuse to take payment for healing and those who do usually make only a modest charge –
far less than a patient would pay if consulting a private medical specialist. They are healers first and foremost because,
having discovered their gift, they believe they must use it for
the good of mankind. Their reward is to see the happiness it
brings to others. So, for them, healing is an expression of
love.

'You can't measure love in a laboratory,' says British
healer Matthew Manning, 'but you *can* measure its effect on
other people.'

In fact, I believe that many of the healing research programmes I have already discussed provide confirmation of that. Though those involved were asked to send healing or to pray for the subjects – whether animal or human – I suspect the results would have been the same if they had been instructed to send *love*.

Loving prayer went straight to their hearts

A group of twenty-one subjects were asked to take part in a study of the effects of sitting without a back support. As far as they were concerned, the researchers simply wanted to check how their bodies coped with sitting upright on backless chairs or benches. They were wired up so that accurate records could be made of their physical reactions. These included electromyographic (EMG) recordings on the forehead and several points on the spine – cervical, thoracic and lumbosacral. An EMG measures the amount of electromagnetic radiation emanating from the muscles, and gives an indication of nervous system activity and muscle tension. The subjects duly took their seats and quietly gazed out through a window across the Sierra Mountains of Northern California.

What they had not been told was that each of them had been randomly selected and assigned accordingly to either a control or treatment group. And they were really taking part in a distant healing experiment. For, at that moment, two healers in the San Francisco Bay area, some 200 miles (320 km) away, were using prayer to send love to the subjects *in the experimental group only*. When the recordings were checked, it was found that there were large reductions in EMG activity in the thoracic and lumbosacral regions of the prayed-for subjects, compared with results in the control subjects. What the monitoring equipment was recording was a large drop in tension and an increase in relaxation in those parts of the body during and following the distant prayer treatment.

Jeffrey Cram, Ph D, of Sierra Health Institute, who led the study, says that yogic theory suggests that such a reduction of muscle energy required to hold up the spine, while being prayed for, may be due to the body's energy withdrawing from the surface into the *nadis* or primary chakra centres. The thoracic region, which experienced a 50 per cent drop in muscle tension at the surface, corresponds with the heart chakra. The evidence suggests, therefore, that the heart is the energy centre most altered by being prayed for – as stated in the ancient yogic teachings known as the *Vedas*, as well as in other spiritual traditions.

The seat of the soul

These findings are reminiscent of Dr Randoph Byrd's research work (described in Chapter Three), in which patients with heart problems were prayed for – again without knowing that they were taking part in an experiment. As William Collinge points out in *Subtle Energies*:

> The outcomes were striking. Those who were prayed for had significantly less congestive heart failure, need for diuretics, cardiopulmonary arrest, or incidence of pneumonia. They were five times less likely to require antibiotics and three times less likely to develop pulmonary oedema. None of the prayed-for patients required intubation (an artificial airway for mechanical ventilation), while twelve of the others did. Also, fewer of those who were prayed for died during the follow-up period.

Both these studies, Collinge suggests, 'point to the heart, as if the heart centre is somehow the portal or antenna through which distant prayer enters to impact the body.' In the first study, the effects were seen in the heart's energy field, and in the second in its physiology. 'The findings,' he adds, 'are, of course, consistent with all our imagery of the heart as being the seat of the soul and the key to our health and well-being.' Coincidentally, he tells us, scientists now know that 'our heart creates the body's strongest electromagnetic field and that with deep feelings of love, compassion and caring this field actually expands and strengthens'. Each beat of our heart apparently produces a wave of electromagnetic energy that pulses outward in every direction. The heart's energy field is also known to influence every cell of our body throughout our lifetime. So it is hardly surprising to learn that it appears to play a key role in the healing process.

But, as well as transmitting love, the heart also feels the effect of being deprived of love.

The effects of a happy marriage

In an Israeli study 10,000 married men were asked about their relationship with their wives. Their health was then monitored over a period of time and the researchers looked to see if any pattern emerged which might suggest a link between the two. They found that those men who answered most negatively to the question, 'Does your wife show you her love?' were more likely to develop angina pectoris (painful heart spasms).

Happy marriages, on the other hand, promote good health and a longer life. Researchers at Ohio State University made this discovery when they studied the immune systems of 473 women. Those in supportive relationships had the highest functioning immune systems, suggesting that a partner's support reduces the effects of stress on our health.

Just witnessing an act of unselfish love seems to have a similar impact on most people, as another team of researchers discovered at Harvard Medical School. They showed a group of medical students a film of Mother Teresa caring for the poor and suffering in Calcutta. They may not have displayed any emotion on seeing the film, but their bodies could not hide the profound effect it had on them. Tests showed a significant boost in their immune functioning.

Religion's role in health

The same physical benefits are also said to be created by a loving relationship with God or some other religious figure, such as Jesus. A seventeen-year study of church members in Alameda County, California, showed they had a lower mortality rate than non-church members in the community. Such findings are open to different interpretations, but it could be argued that the belief that 'Jesus loves me' or 'God loves me' must be every bit as powerful as 'My wife loves me'. Support for this view comes from another study of 2800 elderly residents in New Haven, Connecticut. It was found that those who were involved in a church were less likely to become medically disabled than those who considered church unimportant.

Churchgoing was also linked to positive mental health in a 1991 review of 200 studies, published in the *Journal of Psychology and Theology*. Its authors concluded that, in general, churchgoers showed lower suicide rates, lower rates of drug use, lower divorce rates, greater marital happiness and lower rates of depression.

Whether these findings are simply due to having a positive interest and involvement in a particular activity – in which case similar health benefits may be found in golf lovers and bridge players – or are really the product of spiritual belief, is unclear at this stage. But some are already satisfied that such studies have a deep, spiritual significance.

'If you had an agent that promised you better health, longer life, protection for your children against drug addiction and alcohol abuse, if it would increase your sense of well-being and afford you a sense of confidence against the perils of life, would you not want that agent?' asked Donna Saunders, speaking at the Spiritual Intervention in Clinical Practice convention held in Washington DC, in 1996. 'If it could be wrapped in a pill, would it not be sold easily and abundantly? That agent is here, and it is called God, religion, spirituality.'

Dr William Miller of the University of New Mexico, a nationally recognised researcher in the field of alcohol and addiction, has also spoken of the great healing effect which religious values can have. He and Dr Scott Walker carried out a study which indicates that the power of prayer, directed to subjects who did not know they were being prayed for, had a very real effect upon their addiction.

Yet another study confirming these findings was published in 1998. In April that year, Dr Harold Koenig and a team at Duke University, North Carolina, published in *The American Journal of Psychiatry* the results of a study they had conducted involving eighty-seven elderly hospital patients who were depressed and suffering from conditions which included heart disease and stroke. They found that the stronger an elderly person's religious beliefs, the faster he or she recovered from depression. They measured each individual's 'intrinsic religiosity', then compared their recovery times with their rating on the scale. 'This is the first study to show that religious faith by itself, independent of medical intervention and quality of life issues, can help older people to recover from a serious mental disorder,' Dr Koenig said. Conventional science can offer no explanation for these results.

Paralysed woman whose prayers were answered

But perhaps the most important finding of all is that caring about others can sometimes improve our own health as well.

Dr Koenig, who is a highly respected researcher in the field of geriatrics, tells of a very healthy older woman who hardly had a day's sickness throughout her life. But in old age she began to suffer from 'creeping paralysis' (Guillain-Barre's syndrome). Eventually, it reached the point where she could communicate only with her eyes. The clergy who visited her had great difficulty communicating but soon established a code of one blink for 'yes' and two for 'no'. Having done that, they still found it hard to know what to say to help this devastated, depressed and helpless woman who was feeling so useless.

Then the visiting pastor had the idea of asking her if she would pray for some of his parishioners since he was so busy. She blinked once to indicate her agreement. So he put the names of various parishioners, who were fellow church members she knew, on a piece of paper and put it where she could see it. The paralysed woman studied it and prayed. A week later the clergyman visited her again and found her whole outlook had changed. She was smiling, no longer depressed, and was clearly happy. What is more, he was able to cheer her more by bringing stories about the unexplained beneficial changes which had occurred in a lot of the parishioners since she had started praying for them.

I wondered, when I heard this story, whether the woman had thought of including herself in those prayers. Possibly not. Helping others with loving thoughts had become more important than her own health problem.

Love, as they say, had found a way.

14

HEALING IN THE
TWENTY-FIRST CENTURY

Medical science has made tremendous strides in the last 100 years, with transplant operations becoming commonplace, new drugs being developed that can shrug off diseases once regarded as incurable, and genetic engineering, though still controversial, promising a wide range of benefits in the twenty-first century. But it isn't enough. Alongside these commendable achievements a totally new approach to health – known as holistic medicine – has also evolved. It embraces a bewildering range of alternative therapies and its growth has been even more spectacular than conventional medicine. Why?

'The public has turned to complementary medicine as refugees from the inadequacies of conventional medicine,' argues Stephen Fulder, author of *The Handbook of Alternative & Complementary Medicine*. 'In the last 20 years,' he points out, using UK figures, 'there has been a 300 per cent increase in health expenditure, and a 50 per cent increase in the percentage of the gross domestic product spent on health. Yet there has been a third increase, to 34 per cent of the population, in those suffering from long-term illness, and a 64 per cent increase in incapacity, or days of certified sickness.'

Our hospitals and doctors' surgeries are often stretched to the limit, yet, largely through government contributions but also directly from our own pockets, we are pouring more money than ever before into trying to achieve good health. In America, the healthcare system costs $2.5 billion *each day*, and total medical costs consume more than 12 per cent of the nation's gross domestic product. Though medical researchers have found new ways of fighting some cancers, half a million Americans will still die from the disease this year, and the director of the National Cancer Institute confirmed in 1994 that 'death rates for several important cancers are going up'.

Faced with escalating costs and increased sickness, many people have turned to what used to be known rather disparagingly as 'fringe medicine' but is now most often called 'complementary medicine', reflecting the fact that the skills of healers, acupuncturists, herbalists and others should complement the work of doctors. Already, in the UK, according to a 1997 survey, half a million people regularly seek the help of its 20,000 registered spiritual healers. This interest is not confined to patients. Fulder's book, packed with statistics, reveals an impressive trend in doctors referring an increasing number of patients to therapists and even developing alternative therapy skills themselves. These include, as we have seen, spiritual healing, and I believe the dawning of the twenty-first century will see an acceleration in this merging of the two approaches.

Recent research in healing and allied fields is likely to force a complete rethink of the entire healing process and the way in which our bodies can be encouraged to work more speedily and effectively. Above all, there will be a growing realisation that we can each play a far more significant role in our own health. We can also expect far greater co-operation between healers and medical professionals. Dr Mehmet Oz, a cardiovascular surgeon at Columbia Presbyterian Medical Centre in New York City, is showing us how. He is so impressed with therapeutic touch that he invites healers into his operating room to use their powers on patients while they are undergoing surgery.

What is more, this new approach to medicine has other benefits, the most important of which is to open our minds to spiritual values that, in the West, have largely been swamped by materialism.

Weighing up the evidence

Looking at the healing case studies and laboratory research results already discussed, there appear to be two possible explanations. The cures and improvements achieved by laying-on-of-hands could be achieved simply by the patient's own mind. *Believing* something is about to happen, as with subjects under hypnosis, produces the expected result – the so-called placebo effect. On the other hand, healing or prayer at a distance suggests very strongly that there is some invisible force at work which is transmitted by the sender and seeks out the subject. A third alternative is that healing miracles are produced by a combination of both.

My own view, having weighed the evidence carefully, is that *healing is all in the mind*.

The reasons, which I confess are mind-blowing, will become obvious as I review the complexities of healing cases, and look at intriguing new research which throws light on the whole mind–body relationship. First, let me illustrate the problems we face, in trying to understand the mechanics of healing, with an account from Harold Sherman, a well-known American psychic. In 1920, Sherman developed a blister on his toe after playing tennis but did not treat it properly, with the result that the foot became infected. His doctor, Dr Garner, gave him medication but gangrene set in and began spreading. When a surgeon examined the foot he said it would have to be amputated unless there was a dramatic improvement by the following morning.

Sherman knew that the mind's power could affect the body and had therefore been trying to visualise the toe looking healthy again, but he confided in Dr Garner, 'I don't have the mental strength to rise above it. I feel I need the help of a healthy mind in a healthy body . . . Doctor, when you get home tonight, will you sit quietly by yourself and picture in your mind what has to happen to my toe to make it well?'

The doctor concurred, and Sherman's landlady, who heard this conversation, volunteered to do the same. They agreed that the 'thought healing' would take place between 10pm and 10.30pm and when the appointed hour arrived he prepared for the experiment.

'I relaxed my body as best I could and made my mind passive,' Sherman wrote years later:

> Then, as I had tried countless times before, I sought to see a picture of a healthy toe. Instead, all that registered was this toe in its infected state . . . I knew that Dr Garner in his home, and Mrs Walker nearby, were both visualising, so I let go of this wrong picture and tried again and again, but each time the picture was unchanged.
>
> However, at twenty minutes past ten something happened:
>
> Suddenly, it seemed as though I had tuned in on the positive thoughts that were being projected towards me. For just an instant I glimpsed a fleeting picture of my toe as it had been before the infection. The mental relief was so great that I fell asleep and slept the night through for the first time since this gangrene had developed.

When Sherman woke next morning, 'the swelling was almost gone and I had no pain. Not only that, I had no fever.' Though it took many more weeks before the toe was completely cured, the dramatic overnight improvement was incredible. Dr Garner corroborated Sherman's story with this testimony: 'In more than 40 years of medical practice, this was the nearest thing to a miracle that I have seen.'

But who was responsible? Did Sherman's mind overcome the mental blockage he had experienced earlier and trigger this self-healing? Or did the healing thoughts of his doctor, his landlady, or both, achieve the desired result?

Forgetful healer produces a cure

Let me share with you a similar story but with an unexpected twist. It comes from physicist Lawrence LeShan, an active healing researcher for many years, who also developed his own healing powers. Unable to meet a particular patient in person, he agreed to give him distant healing at a specific time. Later, the man's physician contacted LeShan and explained that he had recovered completely from his condition and no longer needed the surgery that had been considered essential. He was invited to write up this remarkable case of absent healing for a medical journal. Though delighted to learn that the man – who had been many miles away at the time of the test – had made such a remarkable recovery, an embarrassed LeShan had to confess that he could take no credit. He had forgotten all about the agreement and had not sent any absent healing to him. In LeShan's view, whatever the truth of other cases, this one proved that some patients largely heal themselves.

But there is a possibility that LeShan's mind *did* play a part, without him realising it. Remember the story quoted in Chapter One of the great British healer Harry Edwards, whose records were destroyed during the second World War. Without them, he could not remember to whom he should be sending absent healing, or the time agreed. But, instead of the healing results declining, they actually improved. Again, it could be argued that it was his clients' minds that were achieving the results, because they were oblivious to Edwards' inability to send out healing thoughts. But I suspect that their minds, *and Edwards'*, were involved.

Some healers have told me that it is enough for them to read the letters they get from distant people seeking their help for the wheels to be set in motion. The compassion that the healer feels when he learns about the patient's condition is enough, I suspect, for his subconscious to establish the necessary link with the subconscious of the person seeking his help. The healer and the patient may later perform some ritual at an agreed time and that may, in turn, reinforce the belief of either of them – or both. But my view is that the healing begins from the moment the healer first learns about the patient.

Probing the mind's powers

Many of the findings of modern mind research were anticipated over a century ago by individuals whose own experiments make fascinating reading. One of these pioneers was Phineas Parkhurst Quimby, a clockmaker of Portland, Maine, whose mesmeric healing skills attracted many followers in mid-nineteenth-century New England. Born in 1802, the son of a blacksmith, Quimby learned mesmerism but had indifferent results until he discovered a remarkable young subject named Lucius Burkmar, a psychic, who went quickly into a deep trance. While under hypnosis, the nineteen-year-old proved to have impressive healing and diagnostic powers, as this account by Quimby indicates:

> I had pains in the back which, they said, were caused by my kidneys. Under this belief, I was miserable enough to be of no account in the world . . . On one occasion, when I had Lucius asleep, he described the pains I felt in my back (I had never dared to ask him to examine me there, for I felt sure my kidneys were nearly gone), and he placed his hand on the spot where I felt the pain. He then told me that my kidneys were in a very bad state – that one was half consumed, and a piece three inches long had separated from it, and was only connected by a slender thread.

When Quimby asked the entranced Lucius if there was any remedy, he replied, 'Yes, I can put the piece on so it will grow, and you will get well.'

Quimby's statement continues: 'He immediately placed his hands upon me, and said he united the pieces so they would grow. The next day he said they had grown together, and from that day I never have experienced the least pain from them.'

How had Lucius achieved that remarkable result? After much thought, Quimby decided that, had Lucius said there was nothing he could do, he would have died within two years. 'But, when he said he could cure me in the way he proposed, I began to think, and I discovered that I had been deceived into a belief that made me sick.'

In other words, it was all in his mind. He soon realised, however, that the mind – and particularly Lucius's mind – could achieve far more than anyone would have thought possible. Among the many testimonies to Lucius's extraordinary powers, which were sent to Quimby at that time, was the following:

> I have good reason to believe that he can discern the internal structure of an animal body, and if there be anything morbid or defective therein, detect and explain it. The important advantage of this to surgery and medicine is obvious enough. He, that is his intellect, can be in two places at the same time. He can go from one point to another, no matter how remote, without passing through the intermediate space.

It soon became clear to Quimby that Lucius was also capable of reading the minds of people around him. 'This I found out by thinking of something Lucius could describe so that I knew he must see or get the information in some way.' When Quimby visualised a wild animal, Lucius received the image so realistically that he was terror-stricken even after being told it was merely Quimby's imagination that had summoned up the image.

Lucius, when in trance, was able not only to diagnose patients' illnesses but also to prescribe remedies to treat them. In time, Quimby decided to try developing these abilities himself, but without mesmeric intervention, and he did so remarkably well. 'At first I found that my thoughts affected the subject,' he wrote, 'and not only my thought but my belief. If I really believed anything, the effect would follow whether I was thinking it or not ... I found that belief in everything affects us, yet we are not aware of it.'

His healing inspired Christian Science

Quimby is an important figure in the early quest for a better understanding of the mind–body relationship, but he is most often mentioned these days because one of the patients he treated successfully was a Mrs Mary Baker Patterson, the wife of a dentist. Dr Patterson wrote to Quimby in 1861 explaining, 'My wife has been an invalid for a number of years; is able to sit up but a little, and we wish to have the benefit of your wonderful power to be carried to her hotel bedroom.' Mrs Patterson confessed years later that when she was taken to see Quimby she was in a state of physical and mental depression and the hope of a recovery had long 'died out of the hearts of those who were most anxious for it'. But 'in less than two weeks from that time I ascended a stairway of 182 steps to the dome of City Hall'. Many years later, after she had remarried, she wrote for Quimby's help once more, but he had died. She was forced to take matters into her own hands, and heal herself. And that, it seems, is how Mary Baker Eddy came to establish the Christian Science Church, embodying in its 'science of mind' many of Quimby's self-healing concepts.

Healing by 'silent suggestion'

Another man with extraordinary powers, who practised in Massachusetts around the turn of the century, was C.M. Barrows, who was medically unqualified. What was so unusual about Barrows was that his method of treating the sick was to do precisely nothing – or so it seemed. Mrs Agnes Lynch, one of his grateful patients, explained: 'Mr Barrows did not hypnotise me or do anything which I could see or feel. He sat down beside me for about fifteen minutes, and the pain was gone.'

Another testimony, written by Mrs James Honey ten months after she consulted him with a painful finger joint, explains that Barrows examined the joint and asked her some questions about it. 'He did nothing to the finger, but was quiet for not longer than three minutes, I should say, when all pain stopped, and I have had none of it since.' And an illiterate Irishman (who dictated his account of a visit to Barrows eighteen months later) had been 'so lame that it hurt me to sit down'. Barrows questioned him from several feet away. 'Then he stopped talking for two or three minutes, and I don't know what he did, but all the pain left me.'

Barrows seems to have been as puzzled as his patients about the technique he used – which he called 'silent suggestion' – explaining: 'I use neither voice nor other means to convey its importance to the patient through sensory adits [an 'archaic word, meaning 'entrance'], Barrows added, 'The conclusion seems well-nigh irresistible that therapeutic suggestion, as I use it, is not sensory but telepathic, that the communication does not require an act of thinking or willing to send it forth.' And, having done some telepathic experiments himself, Barrows noticed that he was most successful when he made 'no thought effort, no conscious effort of any kind'.

Dr Frederick Knowles, an Englishman whose early career was spent largely in India, developed similar silent methods of treatment, but these were at first based on a traditional yoga healing technique which involved the channelling of 'prana', a vital substance similar to bio-energy. He soon found, however, that he could relieve pain without all the rituals he had been taught. All that was required was a decision on his part to remove the pain. Intrigued as to why this happened, and wondering if it was due in part to his patients' expectations, Dr Knowles experimented by standing outside a patient's field of vision. He did nothing at all for 'much longer than the duration of a usual treatment' but the person complained that the 'treatment' was doing him no good. 'After that,' Knowles continues, 'a brief spell of the usual mental effort brought the usual relief . . .'

Dr Knowles helped such patients with nothing but 'the effort of my will', though he found it to be ineffective if the patient was not aware of his intention. 'It seemed that by themselves, neither the patient's expectation nor my mental

effort were adequately effective. Both together were needed
for the high proportion of successes to which I was accus-
tomed.' After due deliberation, the doctor came to this conclusion: 'My hypothesis is that a physician's thoughts can
affect a patient by a parapsychological process.'

Brain waves record healing effects

Inevitably, researchers began to wonder if there was some
way of capturing this healing effect, or witnessing the communication between healer and patient, scientifically. This
was very much in the mind of Professor Fred Lorenz of the
Department of Animal Physiology at the University of
California, Davis, when young British healer Matthew
Manning first went to the USA to demonstrate his psychic
powers.

In his book *No Faith Required*, Manning tells how Lorenz
and his colleague Professor Loring Chapman decided to use
an electroencephalogram (EEG) to assess the level of brain
arousal during his attempts to influence volunteer subjects
from a distance. Interestingly, Lorenz himself decided to be a
subject and so he went to an isolation room, some distance
from Manning, to be wired to an EEG also. 'The results were
startling,' says Manning.

Under instructions from Lorenz, Manning was told either
to make the professor sleepy or to wake him up. The readings
from both EEGs were compared and were found to be
remarkably similar. 'I was very aware of being alerted three
times,' Lorenz reported, 'with drowsy or inattentive periods
between . . . My first remembered alerting was most dramatic
and seemed to come out of deep drowsiness or even actual
sleep.' Manning, for his part, tried to send a feeling of sleepi-
ness through the wall to Lorenz, and when instructed to
make his mind more active, imagined that he was running
into Lorenz's room shouting, 'Fire, fire!'

'The correspondences between Matthew's EEG and my
own were most dramatic,' Lorenz explains. 'These are most
clearly illustrated by moments such as those where trains of

high amplitude or slow waves are simultaneously evident from both heads. Especially interesting was a kappa rhythm which manifested simultaneously in both heads. The kappa rhythm is usually a sign of alerting during a drowsy state.'

Later, during a visit to Canada, Manning was again wired to an EEG, this time at the Toronto Hospital for Sick Children, so that his brain activity could be monitored while trying to bend metal paranormally. He was also linked to an electromyograph which would detect the slightest physical movement he made. Dr Joel Whitton, a child psychiatrist who was conducting the experiment, found, according to Manning's account in *In the Minds of Millions*, 'something quite new'. This was a brain pattern which 'had a massive ramp-like feature', and which Whitton named the 'ramp function'.

'It was clear,' says Manning, 'that the electroencephalograph caught the surge of energy, or whatever it was, in the brain, that caused the key to bend . . .'

Unusual brain activity has also been reported with other healers, including Dr Dolores Krieger, the originator of therapeutic touch. She was wired to an EEG machine, as well as a variety of other devices to measure pulse, skin temperature and galvanic skin response, for example, and while giving healing it was discovered that her brain produced an unusual number of beta waves (fast waves which occur when a person concentrates on an intellectual task). Even though her body appeared to tense up during the session, her brain waves seemed to be independent of this physical change.

Dr Krieger agreed to do this test while visiting the Langley Porter Neuropsychiatric Institute in San Francisco. Dr Joe Kamiya – one of America's leading authorities on psychophysiology – and several graduates had been keen to monitor what happened during healing. On the second day, incidentally, they also hooked up three patients to check out what was happening in their brains, but they showed no significant shift. Even so, they experienced remarkable improvements. The first, an elderly gentleman, dispensed with his crutches for the first time in months and walked out of the hospital. The second patient's tumours suddenly vanished. And the severe migraine which had afflicted the third patient diminished after the treatment.

Healer produces 80-volt surge of power

In his book *The Uncommon Touch*, Tom Harpur tells of experiments carried out by Dr Elmer Green and Professor Steven L. Fahrion, of the Menninger Clinic, on Mietek Wirkus, a talented Polish healer who now lives and works in the USA. 'This man has spent more hours rigged up by wires to state-of-the-art machines than any other healer I know,' Harpur writes, adding:

> I have seen the evidence and witnessed the corroborating
> testimony of the parents of three very young children –
> one with cataracts which threatened blindness, one with
> chronic cardiac problems (four open-chest operations in
> the year between the ages of two and a half and three
> and a half), and one with uncontrollable epileptic
> seizures (more than a hundred a day) – where the
> healer's intervention made a dramatic difference.

But it is the results of scientific scrutiny, and Wirkus's brain wave patterns, that are of particular interest:

> Isolated from all extraneous electrical and other
> influences in a laboratory room with copper walls,
> Wirkus was meticulously monitored as he carried out
> his healing on a series of healees . . . Dr Elmer Green
> and Professor Fahrion recorded sudden electrical surges
> in Wirkus that on a number of occasions registered 80
> volts or more. These surges were synchronous with
> times when the healer (who was not at all surprised by
> the findings), in his own words, 'was just conscious of
> creating a charge and sending it'. As Green says,
> creating an electrical force of that magnitude 'isn't
> really possible. But it happens!'

Clearly, whatever healers do when they send out healing thoughts appears to produce unusual brain wave patterns – in some at least. And healers also seem to be capable of changing the brain wave activity of the persons receiving treatment, even when there is a considerable distance between them. It seems that a form of telepathy, or mind-to-mind communication, is happening when healing takes place. Some readers may resist such an idea, believing that telepathy should be lumped together with alien abductions and the Loch Ness monster in a file marked 'fantasy'. But I am convinced that the evidence for telepathy is now so strong that science will soon have no option but to remove from this phenomenon the tag 'paranormal' and replace it with one which reads 'normal'.

Hypnotised subjects obey mental instructions

As mentioned in Chapter Two, a team of scientists at Edinburgh University announced striking new evidence for telepathy, or extra-sensory perception – ESP – in 1997.

Over sixty years before this, a Russian scientist, Dr Leonid L. Vasiliev, and his Leningrad colleagues, had reached the same verdict after conducting 260 laboratory experiments. Dr Vasiliev, a corresponding member of the Soviet Academy of Medicine, Chairman of Physiology at the University of Leningrad and holder of the Lenin Prize, was a highly respected Soviet scientist who believed 'the discovery of the energy underlying ESP [would] be equivalent to the discovery of atomic energy.' And the Soviet government poured millions of roubles into such research as part of its Cold War quest for supremacy over the West.

What makes Dr Vasiliev's experiments so important – and they cry out to be repeated by others today – is that they used telepathy and hypnosis over considerable distance. Time and again, the subjects of these experiments would be given mental instructions: 'Cross your legs.' 'Raise your right hand.' 'Walk forward.' And they obeyed those unspoken commands far too often for it to be dismissed as coincidence. In a typical experience with a responsive patient in the summer of 1937, Vasiliev reported, 'Out of thirteen tasks telepathically commanded, six were carried out with total accuracy; there are doubts about three; four weren't carried out.' In some experiments, where more than one person gave mental orders, the hypnotised subject was even able to identify who had asked for a particular movement or action to happen.

Towards a theory of healing

It seems reasonable to say, on the basis of the available evidence, that, though some invisible forces may be at work when healing takes place, a form of *telepathy* could be the driving force behind all healing. Let me explain. Few people would dispute that when we enter an altered state of consciousness, such as hypnosis, we can make our body do things it would not normally do. It can get rid of warts, for example, or dramatically reduce the effects of burns, and even stop us feeling pain.

The problem for most of us is that we need someone – a hypnotist – to put us into that altered state and then give us instructions. If telepathy between conscious minds is a fact, however, then perhaps it involves a very similar mechanism but at a subconscious level. Instead of hearing a hypnotist's voice telling us how to react, our minds receive a message from the healer's mind, and we act on it. *We heal ourselves*, having been instructed to do so by the healer or person praying for us. But the degree of success may depend, in part, on the healer's confidence in his or her powers and also in our openness to the healing suggestion. If there is a good 'connection', so to speak, the message gets through loud and clear and a rapid result is achieved. But if there's 'interference' on the line, or the reception is blocked in some way, the strength of the signal becomes diluted.

The unusual brain wave patterns and surges of electricity exhibited by some healers could all be part of the telepathic process, producing signals which are unusual enough to make an impact on the subconscious mind of the receiver.

This could also explain how distant healing finds its way over thousands of miles. If healings are produced by a force of some kind, I find it hard to envisage how it can travel to its destination, and find the particular individual in need of healing. I find it marginally easier to imagine that we are all hooked up, as it were, on a mental level, to some huge telepathic communications network or Internet system, in which we each have an individual number or address. I have a friend on the other side of the world. If I pick up my phone and dial her number, I can be speaking to her in a matter of seconds. Perhaps, in some mysterious way that we do not yet comprehend, we each have a unique identification code on the global mental network, and if someone just thinks of us our subconscious minds are automatically 'dialled up' and notified.

This is not mere conjecture. Three separate researchers have shown that subjects' finger blood volumes changed significantly when senders, sometimes thousands of miles away, thought about them. Our bodies do react to other people's thoughts. This phenomenon is also said to be the basis of the old wives' tale that when your ears 'burn' (get red or hot), someone is talking about you.

Intuition guides healer's minds and hands

It follows that if a patient can receive a telepathic instruction to get better from a healer, then by the same token the healer ought to be able to receive information telepathically from the patient's mind. This, I believe, explains the ability of many healers to diagnose illness with uncanny accuracy, and why a number of doctors are now cultivating the gift. Dr Daniel Benor, for example, tells of the first healing he witnessed. He attended a psychic fair with a doctor friend and they watched as a healer, Ethel Lombardi, treated various people. One was a young man who revealed a small, hard cyst beneath his left nipple. Benor and his friend stepped forward, identified themselves, and asked if they could examine it. Both the healer and patient agreed, and the two doctors confirmed it caused the man pain when touched, and that it was fixed rather than mobile under the skin.

During healing, Lombardi suddenly said to the man, 'I'm getting the sense that there is some unfinished business between you and your father.' He nodded, said 'Yes', and then began to sob for a long time. The treatment lasted half an hour, after which Benor and his colleague examined the cyst again. According to Benor:

> We were amazed to find that the lump was already less
> than half its original size. What's more, it was no
> longer tender or sore, and it was soft and completely
> non-fixed. I know that if I had not had another doctor
> there to verify my own examination I would have
> begun to think I must have made an error or
> miscalculated in some way. It was a very impressive
> change and improvement.

Benor does not speculate whether the release of emotion which followed the healer's intuitive knowledge about the young man's father contributed to the healing process.

A number of medical professionals are now using the services of gifted individuals to help them diagnose their patients' problems more quickly and efficiently. For several years Dr C. Norman Shealy, a neurosurgeon (who was Director of the Pain Rehabilitation Institute at St Francis Hospital in LaCrosse, Wisconsin) conducted experiments which showed that psychic diagnosticians were more accurate than their medical peers. Caroline Myss achieves her psychic diagnoses by 'observing' a patient's energy field and works with Dr Shealy, giving workshops with titles like 'Energy Anatomy' and 'Learning the Language of the Human Energy System'. Illness, she believes, stems from harmful perceptions, attitudes and stress patterns.

Meanwhile, another teacher of psychic diagnosis, New York healer and former physicist Barbara Brennan, encourages her pupils to develop a 'High Sense Perception' to observe their clients' auras. Brennan contends that all disease originates from psychological and spiritual problems, and that negative emotions and thoughts, childhood traumas and injuries all manifest as blocks in the flow of energy in a person's aura. They also cause distortions in the rotating colours of the chakras, she believes, as they pull vital energy into a person. There are, however, few people who are gifted enough to see such energy in physical form. For most healers, intuition is simply about feeling their hands being guided to the spot where healing is needed.

Guided to save his friend's life

Godfrey Mowatt, the Archbishop of Canterbury's official healer whose story was told in Chapter Five, was also remarkably intuitive. On one occasion he became aware of a sudden, inexplicable urge to call on a friend who he knew was in danger. On his arrival, the butler insisted that the friend was not at home. The blind healer, however, could still sense danger and was positive his friend was in the house. At his insistence, the butler began taking him through the large house from room to room. When they reached the study, they found the friend sitting with a loaded pistol in front of him on the desk. He was preparing to commit suicide, and would certainly have done so but for Mowatt's startling intuition. Had Mowatt been in his mind as he thought over his life? Could Mowatt's mind somehow maintain a 'watching brief' on everyone it had come into contact with? Or was this an example of some outside or even divine intervention?

Sometimes, healing intuition can be extremely forceful. Ambrose Worrall, the American healer whose remarkable abilities have been chronicled earlier in this book, has described how he first gave healing:

> I had a younger sister named Barbara. One day she fell and struck her chin on a table. It was a serious injury. Her neck was paralysed. Or at any rate she was unable to move. Our family doctor tried everything. Specialists were brought in. Nothing worked. Nearly a month

after the accident, I was sitting in the living room reading, and Barbara was sitting in a chair nearby. Suddenly my arms began to feel very strange – as if they were made of lead. They were so heavy I had to put them down on my lap. I had to drop the newspaper. I was frightened at first. Then I felt a sudden compulsion – it was like something pushing me from inside – to get up and put my hands on Barbara's neck. As soon as I touched her, she turned her head, looked up at me and smiled. Her paralysis was instantly ended. I didn't try to explain it, but from then on, whenever I felt this strange weight on my arms I found I could heal people, or at least help them to feel a lot better.

Mind over matter provides another clue

It is now time to take a further leap into the unknown as we try to unravel the mystery of healers and healing. And this time we turn again to Ambrose Worrall and also his wife, the equally talented healer Olga, who were apparently prepared to undergo any test and participate in any experiment, however bizarre, in the interests of science. One of the researchers they worked with was chemical engineer Dr Robert Miller, a former professor at Georgia Institute of Technology, who asked the Worralls to pray and send energy to plants growing in his laboratory. The Worralls did so from their home in Baltimore, 600 miles (960 km) from the plants which were hooked up to a rotary electromechanical transducer and strip chart recorder to measure their growth. During the experiment, Dr Miller and his colleagues reported that in an eleven-hour period the plants grew at the rate of 52.5 mm per hour – which is over 800 per cent more than the normal rate.

From this and similar research with other healers, it seems that the human mind can somehow communicate not only with humans but with other living organisms – in this case plants – and either bring about improvement or inhibit growth, depending on the instruction given. The problem, of course, is that plants do not have minds, so telepathy is *not* the answer. However, plants have cells and other constituents which may be amenable to mental influence at a distance.

Before we explore this possibility further, we ought to consider a far more difficult problem. As part of his research with the Worralls, Dr Miller devised another test, in collaboration with Dr Philip Reinhart, head of the physics department at Agnes Scott College in Atlanta. They wanted to see if the force exerted by healers could influence the path of high-energy nuclear particles as they passed through a special laboratory device, called a cloud chamber, which traces the path of sub-atomic particles. First, the experimenters and several others endeavoured to influence the particles by placing their hands around the chamber. Nothing happened. When healer Olga Worrall placed her hands on the chamber, however, a completely new wave pattern developed. It then followed her hands as she rotated them around the chamber. Even more astonishing, the researchers discovered that she was also able to influence the path of the particles from her Baltimore home.

'We can heal the world'

This, I have to say, suggests very strongly some force in her hands which acted almost like a magnet to interfere with the particles' direction. But there are a number of scientists who believe that the mind is capable of such feats, and that mind over matter is a reality. Dr Robert G. Jahn, of Princeton, USA, has no doubt that the mind can influence matter, after conducting a series of experiments with 100 operators at the university's School of Engineering and Applied Science. The project, which began in 1979, now continues at the Princeton Engineering Anomalies Research (PEAR) programme.

Dr Jahn and his team have used a whole range of machines which, left unattended, behave randomly. Balls tumble down a pegboard haphazardly, for example, and a small motor on wheels runs around indiscriminately. The PEAR scientists monitor this behaviour to confirm that it *is* random, then watch what happens when the mind of an operator attempts to influence the randomness. Time and again, the activities of the machines being 'interfered' with mentally have become less random, with results that are well beyond chance. Operators, who are always out of physical reach of the machine, have devised their own mental methods of interacting with it. The most successful reported a resonance, binding, sharing of identity, even 'falling in love' with the machine.

'All told, 50 million experimental trials have been performed to this date,' Dr Jahn reported in 1995, 'containing more than three billion bits of binary information.' The likelihood that the results they recorded have been caused by chance is estimated to be about one in a billion. What is mind-boggling for most people to come to terms with, and why so many other scientists have so far refused to accept the team's findings, is the fact that significant results were obtained even when the subject was hundreds of miles from the random generator and conducted the experiment *before* or *after* the machine was run for the experiment. What this means is that a subject can decide how he wants to influence the machine *after* the event, and when checked the result is found to be what he intended.

This has some bearing on cases such as those of Edwards and LeShan, discussed earlier, where the individuals did not project healing thoughts at the time they should have, yet impressive results were still achieved. LeShan assumed this meant that his patient's mind produced the cure. But the PEAR research suggests that merely agreeing to send healing at a prearranged time is sufficient for it to happen. There was no need for him to concentrate at that time. More difficult to comprehend is the PEAR claim that an operator's influence can work *after* the event – in other words, that the randomness of a machine changes to conform to the operator's desire, *before* the operator has decided what he wants it to do.

Dr Jahn writes: 'From this huge array of empirical indications, it seems unavoidable to conclude that operator consciousness has been inserting information, in its most rudimentary form, namely binary bits, into these random physical systems by some anomalous means that is independent of space and time.'

The PEAR team have also been conducting remote viewing experiments with equal success and they say their results, which they insist can be replicated, prove that *consciousness can acquire information over vast distances*.

What is particularly pertinent is that, having reached these conclusions, Dr Jahn takes an even bolder step by suggesting how this data could be used to enhance human health. In doing so, he introduces concepts – love and God – which are seldom found in scientific papers: 'Now, if consciousness, via its own expressed desire, can bring some degree of order into a simple random string of ones and zeros emerging from a rudimentary machine, is it so unreasonable to suspect that it can invoke similar, or subtler, processes to influence the far more elaborate, relevant, and precious information processing systems that underlie its own health?'

To do so, he suggests, would require an 'appropriate resonant bond' – and he sees that as love. '*Love!* By scientific experimentation and logic, we have come upon nothing less than the driving force of life and of the physical universe: Love, with a capital "L" . . .' Dr Jahn concludes. 'In essence, then, the *scientific* message is this: "In loving ourselves, we can heal ourselves. In loving others, we can heal the world".'

Heady stuff, but totally in tune with the thinking of many others working in the healing field. Dr Larry Dossey, for example, and other healing experts, now commonly talk about 'non-local mind' when referring to the mind's ability to 'wander' far and wide. Dossey believes the mind is part of a higher 'mental realm' that transcends space and time and in which we have access to potentially unlimited information. He speaks with authority, as the author of *Space, Time and Medicine* and *The Healing Power of Words*, and the publisher of a new periodical, *Alternative Medicine*.

Willis Harman, former director of the Centre for Study of Social Policy at Stanford Research Institute, has said,

'Perhaps the only limits of the human mind are those we believe in.'

And Russell Targ and Jane Katra, in their book *Miracles of the Mind*, remind us of the complexities with which we are dealing:

> It appears to us that qi is a much more complicated matter than we originally supposed it to be. Qi is probably a complicated organic combination of substance, energy, and message. At present, substance, energy and message are studied separately in science. Scientists are very unfamiliar both in theory and in experiments with what conditions will occur when these three produce effects at the same time.

We are all infinite beings

In *Quantum Healing*, Dr Deepak Chopra points out that no one is ever going to find a particle, however minute, that nature has labelled 'intelligence'. He explains:

> This is all the more apparent when we realise that all the matter in our bodies, large or small, has been designed with intelligence as a built-in feature. DNA itself, although acknowledged as the chemical mastermind of the body, is made up of essentially the same basic building blocks as the neurotransmitters it manufactures and regulates. DNA is like a brick factory that is also made out of bricks . . .

Then he adds: 'If intelligence is present in the body, it has to come from somewhere, and that somewhere may be everywhere.' He points to the work of one of the most forward-looking and accomplished researchers in the field of brain chemistry, Dr Candace Pert, director of the brain biochemistry division at the National Institute of Mental Health, who maintains that it is quite arbitrary to say that a biochemical like DNA or a neurotransmitter belongs to the body rather than the mind. DNA is almost as much sheer knowledge as it is matter. In fact, Dr Pert refers to the entire mind–body system as a 'network of information', shifting the emphasis away from the gross level of matter toward the subtler level of knowledge. She prefers to illustrate this unity by referring to *bodymind* in her discussion papers. Dr Chopra believes:

> The possibility that each person is an infinite being is becoming more real now . . . Gifted with total flexibility in our nervous systems, we all have the choice to build boundaries or tear them down. Every person is continually manufacturing an infinite array of thoughts, memories, desires, objects, and so on. These impulses, rippling through the ocean of consciousness, become your reality. If you knew how to control the creation of impulses of intelligence, you would be able not only to grow new dendrites [branches on a nerve cell] but anything else.

Minds that achieve 'the impossible'

What is just as significant, it seems to me, is that we are each capable of *anything* to which we put our minds – particularly as far as our own bodies are concerned – and there is already ample proof of this. In Tibet, for example, Buddhist monks frequently perform 'impossible' feats of physical endurance. The Dalai Lama gave permission for Dr Herbert Benson to study them while they sat meditating, near-naked in freezing temperatures. On one occasion, when the air temperature in their unheated stone huts was only 8 °F above freezing, they wrapped themselves in sheets soaked in cold water. They should have started shivering uncontrollably almost immediately. Instead, they generated enough body heat to cause steam to rise from the sheets and within half an hour the sheets were dry. They repeated this demonstration twice more.

But it is not necessary to go to the foothills of the

Himalayas to witness such powers. A well-known Western Sufi, Jack Schwarz, has repeatedly demonstrated his ability to become insensitive to pain. Researchers have watched in astonishment as he pushes steel sail-maker's needles painlessly through his biceps, without feeling pain, without loss of blood and without the need to sterilise the instrument first. When he is performing this feat, he simply thinks of his arm as not belonging to him and tells it not to interact with, or react to, any foreign material, thus preventing infection. When the needle is removed, the puncture holes close up immediately, leaving virtually no trace of the wound.

There is a wealth of medical evidence, and photographs of Schwarz in action, to prove that what he does is not trickery or sleight of hand. I was reminded of the incredible stories of psychic surgery when I checked my file on him: no pain, no blood, wounds that close up instantly. The similarities are obvious. Could it be that the psychic surgeons – the real ones, that is – have the ability to make their patients impervious to pain and free of infection by conveying that instruction mind-to-mind?

Researcher ends up with dagger in skull

Before rejecting that idea, consider something that happened recently when a team of researchers, led by Dr Jamal Hussein of the Paramann Programme Laboratory in Amman, Jordan, set about studying the followers of a school of Sufi Muslims known as the Tariqa Casanazaniyyah (which means 'the way of the secret that is known to no one'). These Sufi dervishes perform various bizarre rituals involving skewers, spikes and knives which they plunge into their bodies without any obvious sign of pain or discomfort.

The researchers were permitted to conduct various tests, which showed the dervishes were neither hypnotised nor stressed by their experiences. And they were keen to perform their rituals on the investigators. So, physicist Dr Louay Fatoohi of Durham University agreed to go under the hammer, as it were, and allow them to bang a dagger into his skull. He felt the hammer blows, which were strong enough to bend the point, but no pain. And when the dagger was withdrawn from his head there was no blood. This impressive demonstration, and the other tests they carried out, have shed little light on what goes on during these rituals. The researchers suggest that the lack of pain and blood has less to do with the person performing the ritual and more with the beliefs of those around them. But how, precisely, it happens is a mystery.

Biologist baffled by Amazonian healer's antics

Finally, let me leave you with a mystery – concerning psychic surgery – which completely baffles me. There appears to be no acceptable explanation, yet the eyewitness was biologist Dr Lyall Watson, author of the bestseller *Supernature* and other books on the paranormal. He tells, in *Gifts of Unknown Things*, of travelling on a narrowboat up the Amazon when one of his three Brazilian companions developed severe toothache. An abscess beneath a wisdom tooth had become inflamed and the man had a high fever. Having no appropriate antibiotics, Dr Watson tried unsuccessfully to remove the tooth with a pair of the engineer's long-nosed pliers. He was on the verge of calling off the trip and turning back downstream when one of the boatmen explained that a famous healer lived just a few hours up one of the smaller tributaries ahead. When they reached their destination Dr Watson and the patient found the great healer – 'a small, hungry-looking, middle-aged man with little hair and fewer clothes. Just a tattered pair of shorts, sandals and the remnants of a T-shirt'.

Listening to the conversation in Amazonian Portuguese, Dr Watson noted that an agreement was reached which blamed not poor dental care but some malevolent outside influence, an evil spirit force, for the tooth infection. A tightly rolled black cloth was fetched and placed between the patient's feet, but never mentioned again:

Then the treatment began. Singing softly to himself in an Indian dialect, the healer pushed the patient's head back until his mouth was wide open. Then he put his crooked forefinger into the mouth and stirred around in there. He grunted once or twice, peered in again and then reached in with thumb and forefinger and picked out the offending molar as though it were simply lying there loose under the tongue. We all examined the tooth and peered into the empty socket which was bleeding only slightly. There was great satisfaction all round, but the healer wasn't finished yet. He said that he must still get rid of the pain. To do this, he massaged the swollen glands on the patient's throat, then made him sit back again with his mouth wide open.

The healer sat cross-legged on the ground opposite him and began to sway to and fro with his eyes closed. I watched very closely, suddenly aware that this was not just a tired little man in rags, but a very impressive person. Then someone in the crowd hissed and pointed at the patient. A trickle of blood was beginning to flow out the right corner of his mouth and run down his chin. This was not surprising, but what happened next was something that brought a great roar of laughter from all the observers, but made the hair at the back of my neck bristle. Out of the side of his mouth, following the line of the trickle of blood, came a column of live, black army ants. Not a frantic confusion of ants, running in every direction, as they would if the healer had dropped some sort of container holding ants into the patient's mouth, but an ordered column of ants. Ants marching two and three abreast, coming from somewhere and going somewhere.

Dr Watson reports that they kept on coming until there were a hundred or more, moving in a stream down the patient's neck, along his bare arm and down on to the log on which he sat. Then everyone watched the column as it marched off into the grass.

'When the crowd at the healing laughed at the sight of ants crawling out of a man's mouth, it was not the nervous laughter of people in fear or discomfort,' Dr Watson explains:

> It was honest loud laughter over something that struck them as very funny. I didn't see the joke until it was explained to me later. In the local dialect, they use the same word for pain as they do for the army ant. The healer had promised that the pain would leave, and so it did in the form of an elaborate and extraordinary pun. It walked out.

For that patient, in his culture, with his expectations and beliefs, the biologist suggests, the treatment was highly effective. He got better very quickly. Elsewhere – in the Philippines for example – similar paranormal productions are paraded before patients, not because they cure people but because they are deemed necessary to persuade patients that healing has taken place – and their minds do the rest. But how are they achieved? Watson adds:

> For this observer, in his certainty, with his patterns of logic and procedure, the whole affair was shattering. It took me a long time to come to terms with it. It was years before I could even bring myself to talk of it. Who can a scientist tell about an experience like that? But I no longer have that problem. Not since I number theoretical physicists amongst my friends. They have taught me that the objective world in space and time does not exist and that we are forced to deal now, not in facts, but in possibilities. Nobody in quantum mechanics talks about impossibilities any more. They have developed a kind of statistical mysticism which makes physics very hard to distinguish from metaphysics. And that makes things a little easier for a biologist faced with biological absurdities.

CONCLUSION

I am not sure that another century will be sufficient time for us to unravel mysteries like this, but it is clear that the twenty-first century will see an unprecedented reappraisal of healthcare and the role healing can play in it.

There have already been moves by establishment figures to encourage others to take an interest in alternative medicine. Chief among them, of course, is the Prince of Wales who has never shrunk from being counted when it comes to having unconventional interests. Time usually proves him right. In May 1998, for example, he pleaded with the medical profession to have a more open-minded approach to complementary medicine when he spoke at a London conference examining the integration of alternative therapies into healthcare. He also urged alternative practitioners to move towards self-regulation.

'I hope that we shall see an increase in research, not only into the effectiveness and safety of complementary and alternative therapies and how to improve their effectiveness,' said the Prince, 'but also into what people want from their healthcare and why they turn, in particular, to less conventional care.'

The conference was organised by the Foundation for Integrated Medicine which the Prince set up to look into collaboration between orthodox medicine and complementary practitioners. The latest figures indicate that nearly 40 per cent of UK general practitioners now refer their patients for complementary and alternative treatment.

I am also enormously encouraged by the establishment of such bodies as the Doctor–Healer Network, another UK body. It was started by Dr Daniel Benor and is now under the chairmanship of Michael Dibdin, who tells me that two-thirds of its 130 members are doctors and that the healer-members need to have worked with doctors to qualify for membership.

Among its members is Michael Dixon, a GP from Cullompton, Devon, who has worked successfully with healer Gill White for a number of years. The results of an experiment conducted during that collaboration were published in the *Journal of the Royal Society of Medicine*, April 1998. Dr Dixon and his six doctor-partners in the practice sought the co-operation of fifty-seven patients who had a medical condition that had failed to respond to previous treatments for six months or more. He then divided them into batches, taking some from each to receive healing from Gill White and leaving thirty others on an imaginary waiting list. (They were, in fact, 'controls' against whom comparisons could be made).

'The main part of the treatment,' Dr Dixon explained to his medical colleagues in the *Journal*, 'would involve the healer applying her hands close to the patient and slowly moving them over the entire body while visualising the passage of white light passing through her and into the patient.' It was found that the group which received healing benefited from the experience, whereas those who were 'waiting' to be treated showed no change in their condition. Though five of the healing subjects reported no change, eight felt slightly better, seven said they were much better, another six said they were very much better and one reported that he no longer had the symptoms he had suffered with for more than six months before healing was given. In other words, over half the patients felt substantially better after healing – and none felt worse. Though this was a small-scale experiment, it was, says Dr Dixon, 'the first research from primary care to explore the role of a healer in a controlled study'.

He adds: 'The size of effect seen in these chronic patients implies that GPs themselves may have an important thera-peutic role quite apart from the prescription pad or the refer-ral letter, and that we should not underestimate our potential but currently unfashionable role as "physician healers".'

Gill White was working voluntarily in a local hospital, helping to relieve suffering in its pain clinic by the laying-on of hands, when Dr Daniel Benor introduced her to Dr Dixon.

'The hospital association began,' she tells me, 'because I knew the wife of a consultant at the hospital and she men-tioned my name and what I did. I worked there for eight years and have been associated with the Cullompton surgery for six years. But I'm also an Anglican and so I also hold a healing service with the vicar at a parish church near Exeter once a month.' You don't have to be a Christian to be a healer, Gill White adds, but she believes that healers are a channel for the Holy Spirit.

As well as building up a fund of knowledge and creating a framework that encourages doctors and healers to work together, a number of the Doctor-Healer Network's members have begun establishing links with overseas practitioners, particularly in America and Japan.

But possibly the most significant development has been the appearance of doctors and scientists who have also developed healing skills. They include Barbara Brennan, a former NASA scientist, who draws on both her training as a physicist and her insights as a healer to treat the sick and train other heal-ers. Such individuals demonstrate that it is possible to embrace both science and the subtler world of spiritual heal-ing – which is just as well, because some of the theories now being offered as explanations for how healing works, are mind-boggling.

Dr Daniel Benor, the Network's founder and author of the impressive *Healing Research*, is also both a psychiatrist and a healer. His treatment draws upon a range of skills, from hyp-notherapy to acupressure techniques, and from meditation to spiritual healing. Now based in Philadelphia, he lectures and leads workshops for doctors, nurses, healers and others involved in 'holistic and spiritual approaches to caring, health and personal development'. He tells me that he continues to explore ways of introducing healing into conventional medicine and psychotherapy.

For Dr Jordan Weiss, a general psychiatrist, it was a fall from a tree in November 1986 which led him to discover his healing powers and other unusual talents. After the fall he began to hear voices which told him he was to write a book. 'I had often seen patients who had heard voices,' he told me, 'and thought they were obviously mentally ill . . . But I was not psychotic and this was not my own thoughts I heard that day. In one minute the whole concept of sanity and psychosis was being challenged.'

As a result of this on-going dialogue, Dr Weiss has developed a form of comprehensive physical and mental therapy which he calls psychoenergetics, or healing. He has also displayed the courage to speak openly and write about his experiences, knowing that to many they will sound too fantastic to be believed, and that he – as a psychiatrist – would also have been dismissive if a patient had come to him with a similar story.

For those with a scientific frame of mind, there are many questions for which the doctors must find answers. For the majority of healers, however, and those they treat, it is the end result that matters – not how it was achieved.

I have examined case studies and interviewed healers, referred to scientific investigations and considered the possibility of fraud or misinterpretation of data. I have shared with you some of the anecdotal accounts I have unearthed, as well as my own experiences of healing and healers. It is an enormous and fascinating subject with implications that go far beyond our wildest dreams.

It seems that we are returning to our roots: to the desire to take responsibility for our own healing and to appreciate that we can play a far more significant role in our own well-being than we may hitherto have imagined. And probably the most significant finding is that we are all, ultimately, healers.

BIBLIOGRAPHY

Balcombe, Betty, *As I See It*, Piatkus Books, 1996

Becker, Dr Robert, *Cross Currents: the perils of electropollution; the promise of electromedicine*. J.P. Tarcher, 1991

Becker, Dr Robert, *The Body Electric*, William Morrow, 1985

Benor, Dr Daniel, *Healing Research, Vols 1–4*, Helix. 1993

Benson, Dr Herbert, *Timeless Healing: the power of biology and belief*, Simon & Schuster, 1996

Benson, Dr Herbert, *The Relaxation Response*, Avon Books 1976, 1990

Bruyere, Rosalyn L, *Wheels of Light*, Simon & Schuster, 1994

Canfield, Jack & Hansen, Mark Victor, *Chicken Soup for the Soul*, Health Communications, 1995

Chapman, George & Stemman, Roy, *Surgeon From Another World*, The Aquarian Press, 1978

Chesi, Gert, *Faith Healers in the Philippines*, Perlinger, 1981

Chopra, Deepak, *Quantum Healing*, Bantam Books, 1989

Collinge, William, *Subtle Energies*, Warner Books, 1998

Cousins, Norman, *Anatomy of An Illness*, W.W. Norton, 1979

Cowens, Deborah, *A Gift for Healing*, Piatkus Books, 1996

David, Furlong, *The Complete Healer*, Piatkus Books, 1995

Dooley, Anne, *Every Wall A Door*, Abelard Schuman, London, 1973

Dossey, Dr Larry, *Healing Breakthroughs*, Piatkus Books, 1991

Dossey, Dr Larry, *Space, Time and Medicine*, Shambala, 1982

Dossey, Dr Larry, *The Healing Power of Words*, Harper, 1993

Edwards, Harry, *Thirty Years a Spiritual Healer*, Herbert Jenkins Ltd, 1968

Edwards, Harry, *The Power of Healing*, Tandem, 1967

Fulder, Stephen, *The Handbook of Alternative & Complementary Medicine*, Vermilion, 1997

Fuller, John, *Arigó: Surgeon of the Rusty Knife*, Thomas Y. Crowell Co, 1974

Harpur, Tom, *The Uncommon Touch*, McClelland & Stewart Inc, 1995

Jarmon, Dr Robert, *Discovering The Soul*, A.R.E. Press, 1997

Keeton, Joe, *The Power of the Mind*, Robert Hale, 1988

Kilner, Dr J Walter, *The Human Aura* (new edition of *The Human Atmosphere*), University Books, 1965

Lewis, Dr David C, *Healing: fiction, fantasy or fact?*, Hodder & Stoughton, 1989

MacDonald, Allan, *A Path Prepared*, self-published

Manning, Matthew, *In The Minds of Millions*, W. H. Allen, 1977

Manning, Matthew, *No Faith Required*, Eikstein Publications, 1995

Manning, Matthew, *The Link*, Colin Smythe, 1974

McGee, Dr Charles T. & Chow, Effie Poy Yew, *Qigong: miracle healing from China*, Medi Press, 1996

McKenna, Paul, *The Paranormal World of Paul McKenna*, Faber and Faber, 1997

Mishlove, Dr Jeffrey, *The Roots of Consciousness*, Marlow & Company, 1993

Mitchell, Edgar, *Psychic Exploration: a challenge for science*. G. P. Putnam's Sons, 1974

Myss, Caroline & Shealy, Dr Norman, *The Creation of Health*, Stillpoint Publishing, 1988

Nolen, Dr William, *Healing: A Doctor in Search of a Miracle*, Random House, 1974

Pellegrino-Estrich, Robert, *The Miracle Man*, Triad Publishers, 1997

Playfair, Guy Lyon, *If This Be Magic*, Jonathan Cape, 1985

Randles, Jenny, *The Strange But True Casebook*, Piatkus Books, 1995

Rogo, D. Scott, *Mind Over Matter*, The Aquarian Press, 1986

Rogo, D. Scott, *Psychic Breakthroughs Today*, The Aquarian Press, 1987

Schul, Bill, *The Psychic Frontiers of Medicine*, Coronet Books, 1978

Simonton, Carl & Stephanie, *Getting Well Again*, Tarcher-St Martin's, 1978

Southwood, Malcolm, *The Healing Experience*, Piatkus Books, 1994

Stanway, Dr Andrew, *Alternative Medicine – a guide to natural therapies*, Macdonald and Jane's, 1979

Targ, Russell & Katra, Jane, *Miracles of the Mind*, New World Library, 1998

TenDam, Hans, *Deep Healing*, Tasso Publishing, 1996

The Institute of Noetic Sciences, *The Heart of Healing*, Turner Publishing Inc, 1993

Watson, Dr Lyall, *Gifts of Unknown Things*, Hodder & Stoughton, 1976

Watson, Dr Lyall, *Supernature*, Hodder & Stoughton, 1973

Weil, Dr Andrew, *Health and Healing*, Houghton Mifflin, 1983

Woolger, Roger, *Other Lives, Other Selves*, Bantam Books, 1988

INDEX